RINGS OF OPERATORS

Mathematics Lecture Note Series

RINGS OF OPERATORS

IRVING KAPLANSKY

University of Chicago

W. A. BENJAMIN, INC.

New York   1968   Amsterdam

RINGS OF OPERATORS

*The manuscript was put into production on June 15, 1968;
this volume was published on August 19, 1968*

W. A. BENJAMIN, INC.
New York, New York 10016

Preface

The origin of the ideas in these notes was the paper [14]. Rickart initiated an attractive program of studying W*-algebras (alias von Neumann algebras, rings of operators) by adding to the axioms for C*-algebras the single assumption that the right annihilator of any element is generated by a projection. He proved, as a consequence, that the right annihilator of any countable subset is generated by a projection. In the latter part of his paper he added a countable chain condition which had the effect of assuring that the right annihilator of any subset is generated by a projection.

In [5] I followed up this clue and assumed the stronger property outright (although—mistakenly I now think—the axiom was presented in a different way). Moreover I showed that large parts of the theory of W*-algebras could be extended to these AW*-algebras. Further developments took place in [6] and [7], and the Ph.D. theses of Berberian, Goldman, Widom, and Wright date from this period.

In early 1955 some arguments concerning the structure of a ring generated by two idempotents were in the air. I noticed their applicability to the problem of proving the crucial "parallelogram law" for projections. With this it became feasible to throw C*-algebras entirely out of the exposition and make the main line of development a piece of pure algebra. (Actually, there was another purely algebraic path which I missed at the time—see §10 for comments on this). In the summer of 1955 I devoted most of a course to carrying out the details. The upshot was that the basic object to be studied was a Baer*-ring: a ring with involution such that the right annihilator of any subset is generated by a projection. The most elementary material was even carried through for Baer rings with no involution assumed. (The designation honors Reinhold Baer, who studied this condition in his book *Linear Algebra and Projective Geometry*). As the series of theorems neared the climax, two additional axioms were added, unimaginatively labelled EP and SR.

S. Berberian took expert notes on the course, and R. Blattner added two valuable appendices. From 1955 to 1968 these notes were available in the Chicago Mathematics Department's Lecture Notes series.

v

At about the same time (the middle 1950's) I encountered the same circle of ideas in a slightly different context [8]. Start with a complete ortho-complemented modular lattice L. With relatively unimportant (but annoying) exceptions, von Neumann's coordinatization theorem applies to exhibit L as the lattice of projections in a regular Baer*-ring. It is now feasible to repeat, nearly verbatim, the arguments in [5]. (In one respect it is even easier, for the parallelogram law is available right at the start.)

However we should make it clear that the main point of [8] is that regularity forces these particular Baer*-rings to be finite (in the technical sense that left and right inverses coincide). We have not included this theorem in the present work. In addition to [8] the reader can consult the closely related exposition in Skornyakov's book [15], or the paper of Amemiya and Halperin [1], where there is a thorough account in purely lattice-theoretic terms and the theorem is generalized several ways.

In this revised edition of the 1955 notes the exposition has been amplified and clarified at a number of points. Four appendices dealing with various auxiliary matters have been added. An oversight in [8] (repeated in [15]) has been repaired. But the main expository change has been to unify as far as possible the two streams of theorems, for it is inefficient to repeat everything, and unsatisfactory merely to say that everything can be repeated. Now in regular Baer*-rings it is ordinary equivalence of projections that is on the agenda; in other Baer*-rings we work with *-equivalence. The way to unify is to have a postulated equivalence. A large part of this work is due to Robert Kibler and forms a portion of his Ph.D. dissertation at Chicago .

Two final points: (1) To streamline the account a bit, the theory of regular Baer*-rings is presented mainly in exercises with (I hope) sufficient hints. In one place (exercises 4-6 of §4) I have deviated from [8], and hope the reason orthogonal additivity of equivalence works is now clearer. (2) I apologize for not treating as a piece of lattice theory the large parts which can be so treated. I can only lamely explain that I find the language of ring theory more congenial. (Even in high school I preferred analytic to synthetic methods!) I leave it to expert hands to make the necessary translation, and I recommend to readers the paper [1] of Amemiya and Halperin and the excellent survey [4] by Holland.

The list of acknowledgments is pleasantly long; to S. Berberian, R. Blattner, and R. Kibler for allowing me to incorporate their work in the revised edition, to the Research Corporation of America for supporting the writing of the 1955 notes, to Fred Flowers for an expert job of typing, to W. A. Benjamin and Co. for their splendid cooperation, and finally to the four federal agencies (Office of Naval Research, Army Research Office, Air Force Office of Scientific Research, and National Scientific Foundation) who have through the years honored my work with their support.

Chicago, April, 1968   I. Kaplansky

Contents

A Note from the Publisher

This volume was printed directly from a typescript prepared by the author, who takes full responsibility for its content and appearance. The Publisher has not performed his usual functions of reviewing, editing, typesetting, and proofreading the material prior to publication.

The Publisher fully endorses this informal and quick method of publishing lecture notes at a moderate price, and he wishes to thank the author for preparing the material for publication.

1. BAER RINGS

Since annihilators play a fundamental role in everything that follows, we begin with the basic definitions and elementary properties of annihilators.

Let A be a ring and S a subset of A. The set of all elements x in A satisfying $Sx = 0$ (i. e., $sx = 0$ for all $s \in S$) is called the <u>right annihilator</u> of S and denoted by R(S). A right annihilator is always a right ideal, and if S is a right ideal, then R(S) is a two-sided ideal. The left annihilator L(S) is defined analogously. In the following theorem we omit the dual statements obtainable by interchanging left and right.

1

THEOREM 1.   Let A be a ring, and let S, T, S_i be subsets

of A.   Then

(1) $S \subset L(R(S))$,

(2) $S \subset T$ implies $R(S) \subset R(T)$,

(3) S and $L(R(S))$ have the same right annihilator,

(4) $R(\bigcup S_i) = \bigcap R(S_i)$.

The proof is left to the reader.

In the statement of Theorem 2 the unit element is

used symbolically: $(1 - e)A$ stands for the set of all $x - ex$.

THEOREM 2.   Let e be an idempotent in a ring A.   Then

$R(Ae) = (1 - e)A$.

Proof. $Ae(1 - e)A = 0$ shows that $(1 - e)A \subset R(Ae)$.   If

$Aex = 0$, then $ex = 0$ and $x = (1 - e)x \in (1 - e)A$.

THEOREM 3.   In a ring A, any two of the following state-

ments imply the third:

(1) Every right annihilator is of the form eA, e an

idempotent,

(2) Every left annihilator is of the form Ae, e an idempotent,

(3) A has a unit element.

Proof. (1) and (2) imply (3). The right annihilator of 0 is A. By (1), A = eA with e an idempotent. Clearly e is a left unit element for A. Similarly (2) implies that A has a right unit element. Hence A has a two-sided unit element.

(2) and (3) imply (1). Given any subset S, we must show that R(S) = fA with f an idempotent. By part (3) of Theorem 1 we can assume that S is a left annihilator, say S = Ae with e an idempotent. Then by Theorem 2, R(S) = fA with f = 1 - e.

(1) and (3) imply (2). This may be omitted by left-right symmetry.

Remark. Let F be a field and let A be the ring of all two by two matrices over F with second row 0. Then A satisfies (1) of Theorem 3, but not (2) or (3).

DEFINITION. A Baer ring is a ring satisfying any two (hence all three) of the conditions of Theorem 3.

Examples. (1) Any ring with a unit element and no zero-divisors is a Baer ring (by default, as it were).

This is a vast collection of rings and the theory to be developed really has virtually nothing to say about them. We shall be headed rather toward rings resembling matrix rings. If we demand that suitable matrices over a given ring constitute a Baer ring, we find much more stringent requirements. See exercises 2 and 3 for pertinent illustrations (warning: these exercises are moderately difficult).

(2) The ring of all linear transformations on a vector space over a division ring.

If we write linear transformations on the right, the left annihilator of a linear transformation T consists of all elements with range contained in the null space N of T. An idempotent with range N will then serve to generate $L(T)$. For a collection of elements we argue similarly on the intersection of their null spaces.

(3) The ring of all bounded operators on a Hilbert space. That this is a Baer ring is argued just as in example 2. The important thing here is that suitable subrings are also Baer rings.

(4) As a generalization of examples 2 and 3 consider a pair of dual vector spaces V, W over a division ring,
and let A be the ring of "continuous" linear transformations on V, i. e., linear transformations that have an adjoint on W. The condition that A be a Baer ring is easily
seen to be that the pair V, W be splittable as defined by
Ornstein [13]. For information on splittability, the reader
should consult Ornstein's paper. We would like however to
mention a special case: a theorem of Mackey asserts that
splittability holds if both V and W have countable dimension. The corresponding A (describable as the ring of
$\aleph_0$ by $\aleph_0$ matrices which are both row and column
finite) is therefore a Baer ring.

(5) The complete direct sum (also called the direct
product) of any family of Baer rings is manifestly again a
Baer ring.

An important point is that we need not take all of the
complete direct sum; for instance it suffices to take a subring that includes all the idempotents (see exercise 1).

A very simple example of such a subring (and one
that is a W^*-algebra) is the ring of all bounded sequences

of complex numbers. A more algebraic example is pro-

vided by the ring of all sequences of complex numbers,

subject to the restriction of being real from some point on.

Blending the two thoughts we get the ring of all bounded

sequences of complex numbers with imaginary parts

approaching 0, an example pertinent for the consideration

of real AW^*-algebras.

We begin the theory of Baer rings by proving that the

Baer property is inherited by the "corner" ring created by

an idempotent.

THEOREM 4. If A is a Baer ring and e an idempotent in

A, then eAe is a Baer ring.

Proof. The ring eAe has e as unit element. Given

$S \subset eAe$, write $R_e(S)$ for the right annihilator of S in

eAe. Note that $R_e(S) = eAe \cap R(S)$. We must show that

$R_e(S) = geAe$ with g an idempotent in eAe.

Suppose that $R(S) = fA$, f an idempotent. Evidently

$1 - e \in R(S)$, so that $1 - e = f(1 - e)$, from which ef = efe

follows. Set g = ef. Then g is an idempotent and it lies in eAe.

Since $Sg = Sef = Sf = 0$, we have $geAe \subset R_e(S)$. Conversely suppose $x \in eAe$ with $Sx = 0$. Then $x \in R(S)$, $fx = x$, $x = ex = efx = gx \in geAe$, as required.

THEOREM 5. Every direct summand I of a Baer ring A is a Baer ring; $I = uA$ with u a unique central idempotent.

Proof. The form of I is a matter of standard ring theory. That uA is a Baer ring follows from Theorem 4, or by an immediate direct argument.

THEOREM 6. In any Baer ring the annihilator of a central subset is a direct summand.

Proof. Let S be a subset of the center Z of a Baer ring A. Suppose $R(S) = uA$, $L(S) = Av$, with u and v idempotents. Since S is central, $R(S) = L(S)$, $uA = Av$. Thus $u \in Av$, so that $u = uv$; similarly $v = uv$. We now have $u = v$ so that $uA = Au$ is a two-sided ideal. For any x in A, $ux \in uA = Au$ implies $ux = uxu$; likewise $xu = uxu$; thus $ux = xu$, and u is a central idempotent.

THEOREM 7.   The center of a Baer ring is a Baer ring.

Proof. Let Z be the center of the Baer ring A. For any

subset S of Z we have, by Theorem 6, that $R(S) = uA$

with u a central idempotent in A. Evidently the annihilator

of S in Z is uZ.

If u and v are central idempotents in any arbitrary

ring A we write $u \leq v$ in case $vu = u$. Under this partial

ordering the central idempotents form a Boolean algebra.

If A is a Baer ring, the Boolean algebra is complete. For

let S be a set $\{u_i\}$ of central idempotents in A. Write

$R(S) = (1 - u)A$ with u a central idempotent (Theorem 6).

The claim is that u is the least upper bound (abbreviation:

LUB) of the u_i's. For $u_i(1 - u) = 0$ whence $u_i \leq u$, and if

$u_i \leq v$ for all i then $1 - v$ annihilates all u_i, $1 - v \in (1 - u)A$

and $u \leq v$. By general principles, or by a dual argument,

there is also a greatest lower bound.

THEOREM 8.   Let A be a Baer ring, x an element of A,

and $\{u_i\}$ a family of central idempotents with LUB   u.

Suppose that $u_i x = 0$ for all i.   Then $ux = 0$.

Proof. As we saw above, $(1 - u)A$ is the annihilator of $\{u_i\}$. Hence $x \in (1 - u)A$, $ux = 0$.

THEOREM 9. Let x be an element in a Baer ring. In the Boolean algebra of central idempotents there exists a smallest v satisfying $vx = x$.

Proof. $vx = x$ is the same as $(1 - v)x = 0$. By Theorem 8 there is a largest such $1 - v$ and therefore a smallest v.

DEFINITION. Let x be an element in a Baer ring A. The central cover of x, written $C(x)$, is the smallest central idempotent v in A satisfying $vx = x$ (this exists by Theorem 9). If $C(x) = 1$, x is said to be faithful.

The remainder of this section is devoted to developing, in the context of an arbitrary Baer ring, a decomposition into five parts which originated in the theory of rings of operators on Hilbert space (W^*-algebras). Two classes of idempotents are introduced: abelian and finite. The decompositions are then achieved by several uses of the following sort of argument: an appropriate direct summand of the ring is constructed, and Zornification (using the completeness of the central idempotents) leads us to a maximal object of the desired kind.

DEFINITION. A Baer ring is <u>abelian</u> if all its idempotents are central. An idempotent e is abelian in A if eAe is abelian.

The name derives additional justification from the fact that in the case of AW^*-algebras abelian implies commutative. This is not true for general Baer rings: for instance any division ring is abelian.

The assumption that all idempotents commute is formally weaker but actually comes to the same thing (see exercise 5b).

DEFINITION. A Baer ring is <u>finite</u> if $xy = 1$ implies $yx = 1$. An idempotent e in A is finite if eAe is finite.

Of course we don't mean at all that a finite Baer ring is to have only a finite number of elements (but it is true that a Baer ring with only a finite number of elements is finite in the above sense). The source of the name is the

equivalence relation introduced in §2: an idempotent is

finite if it is not equivalent to a strictly smaller idempotent,

and this is in perfect analogy with set theory.

Note that abelian implies finite; we leave this to the

reader as exercise 6.

DEFINITIONS. An idempotent is _infinite_ if it is not finite.

A Baer ring A is of _Type I_ if it has a faithful abelian

idempotent. A is of _Type II_ if it has a faithful finite

idempotent, but no non-zero abelian idempotents. A is of

Type III if it has no non-zero finite idempotents. A is

purely infinite if it has no non-zero central finite idem-

potents.

If we allow these classes to cut across each other

we arrive at the five primodial building blocks,

I_{fin} : Type I, finite,

I_{inf} : Type I, purely infinite,

II_{fin} : Type II, finite (also written II_1),

II_{inf} : Type II, purely infinite,

III.

A rather large number of decomposition theorems can be stated. We single out the three most important in Theorems 10-12.

THEOREM 10. Any Baer ring is uniquely a direct sum of a finite ring and a purely infinite ring.

THEOREM 11. Any Baer ring is uniquely a direct sum of rings of Types I, II, and III.

THEOREM 12. Any Baer ring is uniquely a direct sum of the five types listed above.

Proof in full detail of these three theorems would entail tedious repetition. We shall instead outline the main technique that is needed, leaving it to the reader to complete the proofs.

Suppose we are given orthogonal central idempotents $\{u_i\}$ with LUB u. Suppose each $u_i A$ is of Type I; thus there exists an abelian idempotent e_i with central cover u_i. Our task is to prove that uA is of Type I. So we

must "string together" the e_i's to produce a suitable e.
(Parenthetically we note that when we later switch to the
context of Baer *-rings, and the e_i's are projections, we
will be able simply to take e to be the LUB of the e_i's).
Our method for doing this is to write the right annihilator
of $\{e_i\}$ in the form $(1 - e)A$. We note first that
$e_i(1 - e) = 0$, $e_i = e_i e$. Set $f_i = ee_i$, noting that f_i is an
idempotent. Next, $eu_i = f_i$. For, let $x = eu_i - f_i$. For
$j \neq i$, $e_j x = e_j u_i e - e_j ee_i$. Since $e_j e = e_j$, and e_j and e_i
have orthogonal central covers, we find $e_j x = 0$. Also
$e_i x = e_i eu_i - e_i ee_i = e_i - e_i = 0$. So x right-annihilates all
the e_k's and it follows that $x \in (1 - e)A$, $ex = 0$. However,
$ex = x$, whence $x = 0$.

The element e has thus strung together not the
given e_i's, but the closely related f_i's. This is good
enough, for we are able to show that $C(e) = u$ and e is
abelian.

$C(e) = u$. For all i, $e_i = e_i u_i = e_i u_i u = e_i u$; hence
$e_i(1 - u) = 0$, $e(1 - u) = 0$, $e = eu$, $C(e) \leq u$. Left multiplication of $e = eC(e)$ by e_i gives $e_i = e_i C(e)$; hence
$u_i \leq C(e)$ for all i and $u \leq C(e)$.

e is abelian. We begin by noting that f_i is abelian. This can be seen as follows: the mapping $x \to ex$ is an isomorphism of the ring $e_i A e_i$ onto the ring $f_i A f_i$ (we are anticipating the theory of equivalence of idempotents; see Theorem 15). Thus the conditions that idempotents are central in $e_i A e_i$ gets transferred to $f_i A f_i$, and f_i is abelian. Now take an idempotent g in eAe. Our problem is to prove g central in eAe, i.e., to prove g commutes with any y in eAe. It suffices to prove gy - yg annihilates u, and for this it suffices to prove that it annihilates each u_i. But gu_i is an idempotent in $f_i A f_i$ and therefore commutes with yu_i, since yu_i lies in $f_i A f_i$ and f_i is abelian. Hence gy - yg annihilates u_i, as desired.

A similar plan is used to prove that if $\{u_i\}$ are orthogonal central idempotents with LUB u, and each $u_i A$ contains a faithful finite idempotent, then the same is true for A.

The final point we mention is proved in a quite straightforward fashion: if $\{u_i\}$ are orthogonal central idempotents with LUB u, and each u_i is finite, then u is finite.

In concluding this section we show that certain additional things are true if we assume that there are no non-zero nilpotent ideals.

THEOREM 13.   Let A be a Baer ring with no non-zero nilpotent ideals. (a) If I is a right ideal in A, then $R(I)$ is a direct summand of A. (b) For x, y in A, $xAy = 0$ is equivalent to $C(x)C(y) = 0$. (c) If e is an idempotent in A and f a central idempotent in eAe, then $f = C(f)e$. (d) If e is an abelian idempotent in A and f is an idempotent in eAe then $f = C(f)e$.

Proof. (a) We have $R(I)$ equal to eA, say. Now the right annihilator of a right ideal is always a two-sided ideal, so eA is a two-sided ideal in A. Hence $Ae \subseteq eA$, and it follows that $(1 - e)Ae = 0$. We now see that $A(1 - e)$ is a nilpotent right ideal and it too must be 0. Hence e is central.

(b) $C(x)C(y) = 0$ always implies $xAy = 0$. Conversely assume $xAy = 0$. By part (a), $R(xA) = uA$ with u a central idempotent. We have $y \epsilon uA$, so that $uy = y$,

$C(y) \leq u$. Also $xu = 0$, so that $x(1 - u) = x$, $C(x) \leq 1 - u$.

Hence $C(x)C(y) = 0$.

(c) For any x in A, $fxf = fexef$ since $f = ef = fe$.

Now exe commutes with f, so $fexef = fexe$ and this is

fxe. Putting these together we have $fxf = fxe$, i. e.,

$fA(e - f) = 0$. By part (b), $C(f)C(e - f) = 0$. Since $C(e - f)$

acts as a unit element on $e - f$ we deduce $C(f)(e - f) = 0$,

i. e., $C(f)e = C(f)f = f$, as required.

(d) If e is an abelian idempotent, all idempotents

in eAe are central. Thus (d) is a special case of (c).

EXERCISES. 1. Let A be a Baer ring. Let B be a sub-

ring containing all the idempotents in A. Prove that B is

a Baer ring.

2. Let A be a ring with unit and no divisors of 0,

and let n be an integer greater than 1. Prove the follow-

ing statements equivalent:

(a) A is a division ring,

(b) The ring of n by n triangular matrices over A

is a Baer ring.

3. Let A be an integral domain (commutative ring with unit and no zero-divisors). Let n be an integer greater than 1. Prove the following statements equivalent:

(a) R is Prüfer (all finitely generated ideals invertible),

(b) the ring of n by n matrices over A is a Baer ring.

4. Let A be a Baer ring. Prove that the set of principal right ideals in A generated by idempotents forms a complete lattice. Prove that the principal left ideals generated by idempotents form an anti-isomorphic lattice.

5. (a) Show that an idempotent which commutes with all nilpotent elements is central. (Hint: argue that e commutes with $eA(1-e)$ and $(1-e)Ae$).

(b) Show that an idempotent that commutes with all idempotents is central. (Hint: $e + ex(1-e)$ is idempotent).

6. If a ring contains elements x, y with $xy = 1$, $yx \neq 1$, prove that it contains two non-commuting idempotents. (Hint: yx is an idempotent. If it is central (see exercise 5) then $xyxy = yx \cdot xy$).

7.   A Baer ring is a factor if its central idempotents are 0, 1.   An idempotent e is minimal if e ≠ 0
and the only idempotents in eAe are 0 and e.

(a) Prove that a minimal idempotent is abelian.

(b) Let e be a minimal idempotent and u its central cover.   Prove that uA is a factor of Type I.

8.   (a) Let A be a Baer ring, e an idempotent in
A, f an idempotent in eAe.   Prove: if f is an abelian
idempotent in eAe, then f is abelian in A.

(b) The same, with "abelian" replaced by "finite".

9.   Prove: a Baer ring contains no non-zero central
nilpotent elements.

10.   Let A be a Baer ring with no non-zero nilpotent ideals.

(a) If A is a factor and e any idempotent in A,
prove that eAe is a factor.

(b) If A is a factor of Type I prove that A contains
a minimal idempotent.

11.   If A is a Baer ring of Type III, and e is an
idempotent in A, prove that eAe is of Type III.

12. (This exercise, together with excercise 7 in
§2, constitutes a preview of what can be done by assuming
the existence of suitable idempotents; in the presence of an
involution we shall later obtain sharper results).

Call A a <u>Zorn ring</u> if for any non-nilpotent x
there exists y with xy a non-zero idempotent e. Alternatively: any non-nil right ideal contains a non-zero idempotent. Note that yex is also a non-zero idempotent, so
the hypothesis is left-right symmetric.

(a) If A is a Zorn ring, prove that fAf is a Zorn
ring for any idempotent f.

(b) Let A be both a Baer ring and a Zorn ring and
suppose its only idempotents are 0,1. Prove that A is a
division ring.

(c) Suppose A is Baer, Zorn and has no nilpotent
ideals. Prove that A is a factor of Type I if and only if it
is primitive with a minimal one-sided ideal.

2. EQUIVALENCE OF IDEMPOTENTS

In this section we shall introduce equivalence of idempotents, prove some basic properties, and establish finite additivity.

The characterization which appears in Theorem 14 will not be used in the future, but the connection with modules is of interest, and Theorem 14 does make it instantly clear that equivalence is indeed an equivalence relation.

THEOREM 14. Let e, f be idempotents in a ring A. The following are equivalent:

(1) eA, fA are isomorphic as right A-modules,

(2) Ae, Af are isomorphic as left A-modules,

(3) There exist elements x in eAf, y in fAe with
xy = e , yx = f .

Proof. Since condition (3) is left-right symmetric it will
suffice to identify (2) and (3).

(3) implies (2). Map Ae to Af by right multiplication by x, Af to Ae by right multiplication by y. The
product both ways is clearly the identity.

(2) implies (3). Let ϕ be the map from Ae to Af,
and set $\phi(e) = x$. Then since ϕ is a module map we have
$\phi(a) = \phi(ae) = a\phi(e) = ax$ for any a in Ae, i.e. ϕ is right-
multiplication by x. In particular, $x = \phi(e) = ex$, and
$x \in eAf$. Similarly the map from Af to Ae is right-
multiplication by an element y in fAe. Evidently xy = e,
yx = f.

DEFINITION. Idempotents e, f in a ring A are equivalent,
written e $\sim$ f, if they satisfy any (and hence all) of the conditions in Theorem 14.

Note that a Baer ring is finite if and only if e $\sim$ 1
implies e = 1.

THEOREM 15. Let e, f be idempotents in a ring A, and suppose they are equivalent via the elements x, y. Then the mapping a → yax is an isomorphism of the ring eAe onto the ring fAf. If g is an idempotent in eAe, then g and its image ygx are equivalent.

Proof. Form the map b → xby from fAf to eAe. It is routine that both maps are ring homomorphisms, and they are isomorphisms since they are inverses of each other. The idempotents g, ygx are equivalent via the elements gx, yg.

COROLLARY. If e, f are equivalent idempotents in a Baer ring then e is abelian (resp. finite) if and only if f is abelian (resp. finite).

THEOREM 16. Equivalent idempotents in a Baer ring have the same central cover.

Proof. Let e, f be equivalent via x, y and write C(e) = u. We have $x \in eAf = ueAf \subset uA$, similarly $y \in uA$, hence $f = yx \in uA$, $C(f) \leq u$. By symmetry we have the other inequality and then equality.

THEOREM 17. In a ring A let $e_1, \ldots, e_n$ be orthogonal idempotents and assume the same for $f_1, \ldots, f_n$. Write $e = e_1 + \ldots + e_n$, $f = f_1 + \ldots + f_n$. Suppose $e_i \sim f_i$ for all i. Then $e \sim f$.

Proof. Let x_i, y_i be elements implementing the equivalence of e_i, f_i. Set $x = \Sigma \, x_i$, $y = \Sigma \, y_i$. It is routine to verify that e, f are equivalent via x, y.

EXERCISES. 1. Prove: If two central idempotents are equivalent, they are equal.

2. Prove: If a ring A contains an idempotent e with $e \sim 1$, $e \neq 1$, then A contains an infinite set of orthogonal equivalent idempotents.

3. Prove the following equivalent for idempotents e, f in a ring with unit:

(a) $e \sim f$ and $1-e \sim 1-f$,

(b) e and f are similar, i.e. there exists an invertible x with $x^{-1} e x = f$.

4. If idempotents e, f in a ring A with unit satisfy $eA = fA$ prove e and f similar.

5. Let e, f be equivalent idempotents in a ring A and let I be a two-sided ideal in A containing e. Prove: $f \in I$.

6. Let e, f be idempotents in a ring with unit and suppose that ef - fe is invertible. Prove: $e \sim f \sim 1 - e \sim 1 - f$. (Hint: it is sufficient to prove $e \sim f$, since $(1 - e)f - f(1 - e) = -ef - fe$ etc. From the identity

$$-(ef - fe)^2 = ef(1 - e)fe + (1 - e)fef(1 - e)$$

and the hypothesis deduce that ef(1 - e)fe is invertible in eAe. From $efe - (efe)^2 = ef(1 - e)fe$ get that efe is invertible in eAe, say with inverse t. Then e, f are equivalent via ef, ft. This exercise is a preview of Theorem 60).

7. (A continuation of exercise 12 in §1.) Let A be a Zorn ring with no nilpotent ideals $\neq 0$.

(a) Let e, f be idempotents in A with $eAf \neq 0$. Prove that there exist non-zero idempotents e_1, f_1 with $e_1 \in eAe$, $f_1 \in fAf$, $e_1 \sim f_1$. (Hint: take $0 \neq x \in eAf$, $xy = e_0 \neq 0$, $e_1 = e_0 e$, $fyxf = f_1$.)

(b) Assume in addition that A is a Baer ring of Type I. Prove that for any idempotent e, eAe is of Type I.

(Hint: apply part (a) to e and f, with f a faithful abelian idempotent.)

8. (a) If u is a central idempotent in any ring A and e is an idempotent equivalent to u, prove e ∈ uA.

(b) If u is further finite, prove e = u.

3. BAER *-RINGS

In the first two sections we explored how far the theory of Baer rings can get without an involution. At this point the deeper theory begins and requires an involution.

DEFINITIONS. An involution * of a ring is an anti-automorphism whose square is the identity. An element x is self-adjoint if $x^* = x$. A projection is a self-adjoint idempotent. A subset S is self-adjoint if $x \in S$ implies $x^* \in S$. A Baer *-ring is a ring A with involution *, such that for any subset S, $R(S) = eA$ with e a projection.

Remarks. 1. By applying the involution we get that in a Baer *-ring the left annihilator of any subset is likewise generated by a projection. Thus (1) and (2) of Theorem 3

27

are satisfied and A has a unit element. In particular:
a Baer *-ring is a Baer ring.

2. The projection e generating eA is unique.
For if eA = fA with e and f projections, we find e = fe,
f = ef = $(fe)^* = e^* = e$.

Because of this uniqueness, we can (and shall) call
e the right-annihilating projection of S. Even more useful
is g = 1 - e which we shall call the right projection of S;
g satisfies the condition sg = s for all s ∈ S and is the
smallest such projection.

3. If f is an idempotent in a Baer *-ring, and e is
its right projection, we readily see that e ~ f. We note a
slight sharpening of this result:

THEOREM 18. Let e and f be idempotents in a Baer
*-ring, f ∈ eAe. Let g and h be the right projections of e
and f. Then e - f ~ g - h.

Proof. Noting that g ≥ h, eg = e, ge = g, fh = f, hf = h, we
verify directly that e - eh and g - gf implement an equivalence of e - g and f - h.

DEFINITION. For projections e, f in a ring with involution write $e \leq f$ in case $e = ef$ (which is equivalent to $e = fe$). One readily sees that this relation makes the projections into a partially ordered set.

THEOREM 19. The projections in a Baer *-ring form a complete lattice.

Proof. Given a family $\{e_i\}$ of projections let e be their right projection. One readily sees that e is the LUB of the e_i's. Dually, there is a GLB.

DEFINITION. Let A be a Baer *-ring, B a subring of A. We sey that B is a Baer *-subring of A if:

(1) B is a self-adjoint subring,

(2) If $S \subset B$ and e is the right-annihilating projection of S (in A), then $e \in B$.

If B is a Baer *-subring of A, then B is itself obviously a Baer *-ring. Its unit element is the same as that of A (take the annihilator of 0). The lattice of projections in B is a complete sublattice of that of A.

If A is a Baer *-ring and e is a projection in A, the projections of eAe are the projections f ∈ A with f ≤ e. It follows easily that eAe is a Baer *-ring, and that a family of projections in eAe has the same LUB whether computed in eAe or in A.

THEOREM 20. Let A be a Baer *-ring, S a self-adjoint subset of A. Let T be the commuting ring of S, i.e. all elements commuting with every element of S. Then T is a Baer *- subring of A.

Proof. Since S is self-adjoint, the subring T is also self-adjoint. Given V ⊂ T, write R(V) = eA (this is the annihilator in A, of course). We must show that e lies in T. Thus, given s ∈ S, we have to prove es = se. Given v ∈ V, we have sv = vx and ve = 0, whence v(1 - e)se = vse - vese = sve - 0 = 0; since v is arbitrary in V, (1 - e)se ∈ eA, (1 - e)se = 0, se = ese. Apply * to get se = es.

COROLLARY. The center of a Baer *-ring is a Baer *-subring.

THEOREM 21. In a Baer *-ring, $xx^* = 0$ implies $x = 0$.

Proof. Let e be the right-annihilating projection of x.
Then $xe = 0$, $ex^* = 0$. Since $xx^* = 0$, we have $x^* \in eA$,
$x^* = ex^* = 0$.

It follows that a Baer *-ring has no nil left or right
ideals. For let I be a nil right ideal in a Baer *-ring. If
$x \in I$ then $y = xx^* \in I$. If y^n is the smallest power of y
that is 0, let $z = y^{n-1}$. Then $zz^* = z^2 = 0$, whence $z = 0$
by Theorem 21. Hence $x = 0$. The argument for a nil left
ideal is analogous.

A fortiori, a Baer *-ring has no nilpotent ideals.
This makes Theorem 13 applicable. The *-version of
Theorem 13 will be so useful that we state it in full.

THEOREM 22. Let A be a Baer *-ring. (a) If I is a
right ideal in A, then $R(I)$ is a direct summand of A.
(b) For x, y in A, $xAy = 0$ is equivalent to $C(x)C(y) = 0$.
(c) If e is a projection in A and f a central projection
in eAe, then $f = C(f)e$. (d) If e is an abelian projection
in A and $f \leq e$, then $f = C(f)e$.

We turn now to the consideration of equivalence of projections in a Baer *-ring.

THEOREM 23. Let A be a Baer *-ring, x an element of A such that xx^* is a projection e. Then x^*x is also a projection f. We have $x \in eAf$, $x^* \in fAe$ and thus $e \sim f$.

Proof. Set $y = ex - x$. Then $yy^* = (e-1)xx^*(e-1) = 0$, whence $y = 0$ by Theorem 21, $ex = x$. If $f = x^*x$ then $f^* = f$, $f^2 = x^*xx^*x = x^*ex = x^*x = f$. We find $fx^* = x^*$ as in the first part of the proof. Thus $xf = x$, $x \in eAf$, $x^* \in fAe$.

DEFINITION. An element x in a ring with involution is called a partial isometry if xx^* and x^*x are projections.

DEFINITION. In a ring A with involution * , projections e, f are called *-equivalent, written $e \overset{*}{\sim} f$, if there exists a partial isometry x in eAf with $xx^* = e$, $x^*x = f$.

It is easily verified that $\overset{*}{\sim}$ is an equivalence rela-tion and that $e \overset{*}{\sim} f$ implies $e \sim f$. Note that if A is a Baer *-ring the condition $x \in eAf$ in the definition of

*-equivalence is redundant (Theorem 23).

The next two theorems are the *-analogues of Theorems 15 and 17. The proofs are similar and are left to the reader.

THEOREM 24. In a ring A with involution $*$ let projections e, f be *-equivalent via the element x. Then the map mapping $a \rightarrow x^* ax$ is a *-isomorphism of the ring eAe onto the ring fAf. The image $x^* gx$ of a projection in eAe is *-equivalent to g.

THEOREM 25. In a ring with involution $*$ let $e_1, \ldots, e_n$ be orthogonal projections and assume the same for $f_1, \ldots, f_n$. Let $e = e_1 + \ldots + e_n$, $f = f_1 + \ldots + f_n$. Suppose $e_i \overset{*}{\approx} f_i$ for all i. Then $e \overset{*}{\approx} f$.

We now wish to make some comparisons between Baer rings and Baer *-rings. We begin by exhibiting a condition (satisfied in any C^*-algebra with unit element) that can convert a Baer ring into a Baer *-ring.

THEOREM 26. Let A be a ring with involution $*$, and suppose that for every x in A, $1 + x^*x$ is invertible in A. Then for any idempotent f in A there exists a projection e such that $fA = eA$.

Proof. Let $z = 1 + (f - f^*)(f^* - f) = 1 - f - f^* + ff^* + f^*f$. By hypothesis, z is invertible, say $t = z^{-1}$. Since $z = z^*$, $t = t^*$ also. We have $fz = zf = ff^*f$. It follows that t commutes with f and also with f^*.

Our choice for e is ff^*t. We compute $e^* = tff^* = ff^*t = e$, $e^2 = ff^*tff^*t = t(ff^*f)f^*t = tzff^*t = e$; thus e is a projection. Evidently $fe = e$ whence $eA \subset fA$; also $ef = ff^*tf = ff^*ft = fzt = f$, and $fA \subset eA$.

COROLLARY. Let A be a Baer ring with an involution $*$, and suppose that $1 + x^*x$ is invertible for every x in A. Then A is a Baer $*$-ring.

Next we give a condition (again satisfied in any C^*-algebra) which identifies the two versions of equivalence.

THEOREM 27. Let A be a ring with involution *. Assume

that for any $y \epsilon A$ there exists a self-adjoint $z \epsilon A$ which

commutes with everything that commutes with y^*y and

satisfies $z^2 = y^*y$. Then equivalent projections in A are

*-equivalent.

Proof. Let the projections e, f be equivalent via x, y:

$x \epsilon eAf$, $y \epsilon fAe$, $xy = e$, $yx = f$. Choose z (relative to y)

as permitted by the hypothesis. We have

$xx^*y^*y = x(yx)^*y = xf^*y = xfy = xy = e$. Since e is self-

adjoint, $xx^*y^*y = y^*yxx^* = e$. Thus xx^* commutes with

y^*y and hence also with z. Since $y^*ye = y^*y$, e commutes

with y^*y (take adjoints); therefore $ez = ze$.

The element $w = ezx \epsilon eAf$ implements the desired

*-equivalence of e and f. For $w^*w = x^*zezx = x^*z^2ex$

$= x^*y^*yx = (yx)^*yx = f^*f = f$, $ww^* = ezxx^*ze = exx^*z^2e$

$= xx^*y^*ye = x(yx)^*y = xfy = xy = e$.

We briefly survey how this section meshes with the

preceding two. Of course a Baer *-ring is, a fortiori, a

Baer ring, so all the earlier results apply. However, in

the presence of the involution we would prefer to state them in terms of projections rather than idempotents. This trans-

lation is quite routine. If e is an idempotent in a Baer

*-ring and f is its right projection then $eA = fA$ and $e \sim f$.

Use of the corollary to Theorem 15 allows us to move from

idempotents to projections. For example, if a Baer *-ring

contains a faithful abelian idempotent then it contains a faith-

ful abelian projection. The handling of central idempotents

is even simpler, for they are automatically self-adjoint.

(If u is a central idempotent, form $v = u(1 - u^*)$, note that

$vv^* = 0$, $v = 0$, $u = uu^*$).

One point is a little harder: the natural *-definition

of an abelian ring is that all projections are central. But

this suffices to insure that all idempotents are central

(exercise 2).

One warning: in talking about finiteness we shall have

to specify whether we mean finiteness relative to equivalence

or *-equivalence. In §§5-12 this will fortunately be irrele-

vant, since we shall be using a postulated equivalence.

A final word about equivalence versus *-equivalence:

In the presence of the hypothesis of Theorem 27 the two are

identical, but this is not always true (exercise 10). In the kind of theory that originated in W^* and AW^*-algebras, it is

*-equivalence that is the natural subject.   But in other con-

texts, notably regular Baer *-rings (called complete

*-regular rings in [8], we study ordinary equivalence.   An

axiomatic treatment is called for to handle both efficiently.

EXERCISES.   1.   Let   A   be a commutative Baer ring.

Show that   A   becomes a Baer *-ring if we set * = identity.

2.   Let   A   be a Baer *-ring in which all projections

commute.   Prove: every idempotent is central.   (Hint: let

f be an idempotent, e its right-annihilating projection,

g its left-annihilating projection.   Get $1 - f \epsilon eA$, $ge(1 - f)$

$= g(1 - f)$.   Since ge = eg, gf = 0, get eg = g.   Similarly

eg = e.   Then e = g, ef = 0, f = 1 - e.   Thus all idempotents

are projections.   Quote exercise 5(b) of §1).

3.   Let the hypothesis on A be as in Theorem 27.

Assume projections e and f are similar $(x^{-1}ex = f)$.   Prove

that e and f are unitarily equivalent (i.e. $u^*eu = f$ where

$uu^* = u^*u = 1)$.

4.   A ring is regular (also called von Neumann) if

for any a there exists an x with axa = a.   Prove that in a

regular ring the right (or left) annihilator of any element
can be generated by an idempotent.

5. Let A be a regular ring possessing an involution *. Prove the following equivalent: (a) the right annihilator of an element is generated by a projection, (b) $xx^* = 0$
implies $x = 0$. (Hint: to prove (b) implies (a) observe that
x and xx^* have the same right annihilator. By regularity
get $x = xx^*y$; x^*y is the required right projection of x).

As in [8] we call a ring satisfying these conditions
*-regular.

6. Prove: in a *-regular ring the projections form
a lattice, and that this lattice is complete if and only if the
ring is in addition a Baer ring (and thus a Baer *-ring).

7. Prove: in a *-regular ring the right and left projections of an element are equivalent. (Hint: if $axa = a$
then $e = ax$ and $f = xa$ are equivalent idempotents, and
$eA = aA$, $Af = Aa$. If g is the left projection of a and h
the right projection of a, then $aA = gA$ and $Aa = Ah$.)

8. Let F be a field, A the ring of n by n matrices
over F, * transposition on A. Prove that A is a Baer
*-ring if and only if $x_1^2 + \ldots + x_n^2 = 0$ implies that each

$x_i = 0$. (Note that in particular the characteristic of F

must exceed n).

   9. Over a field F let V be a finite-dimensional

vector space carrying a non-singular symmetric inner pro-

duct $f(x, y)$. Let A be the ring of linear transformations

on V, and * the adjoint relative to f. Prove that A is a

Baer *-ring if and only if f is non-isotropic, i. e. $f(x, x) = 0$

implies $x = 0$. (Note that exercise 9 is a special case).

   10. Let A be the ring of 2 by 2 matrices over

GF(3), the field of 3 elements. Let * be transposition.

Verify that A is a Baer *-ring. Show that the projections

$$\begin{pmatrix} 1 & 0 \\ 0 & 0 \end{pmatrix} \ , \quad \begin{pmatrix} -1 & -1 \\ -1 & -1 \end{pmatrix}$$

are equivalent but not *-equivalent.

   11. Let B be a ring with involution *. Let A be

the ring of all n by n matrices over B, and equip A with

the involution given by *-transpose: $(b_{ij})^* = (b_{ji}^{\ *})$. Suppose

A is a Baer *-ring. Prove that n is invertible in A.

(Hint: let x be the matrix with 1's in the first row and 0's

elsewhere. Let e be the right projection of x. The equa-

t

tion $xe = x$ shows that the columns of e add up to 1. By taking adjoint, see that the same is true for the rows of e. Let y have 1 in the upper left corner, -1 right beneath, and 0's elsewhere. Then $xy = 0$, $ey = 0$, the first two elements of the first row are equal. In this way, see that all the entries in e are $1/n$).

12. Let A be a Baer *-ring possessing n equivalent orthogonal projections $e_1, \ldots, e_n$ with $e_1 + \ldots + e_n = 1$. Prove that n is invertible in A. (Build a set of *-matrix units around the e_i's, i.e. elements e_{ij} with $e_{ii} = e_i$, $e_{ij}^* = e_{ji}$, $e_{ij}e_{km} = \delta_{jk}e_{im}$. If B is the subring commuting with the e_{ij}'s, A is *-isomorphic with n by n matrices over B, the involution on the latter being *-transpose. Use exercise 11).

13. Under the same hypothesis as in exercise 12, prove that n! is invertible in A.

4. THE AXIOMS

We shall study a Baer *-ring A with a postulated equivalence relation, written $\sim$, on its projections. There are six axioms.

(A) $e \sim 0$ implies $e = 0$.

(B) If $e \sim f$ and u is a central projection, then $ue \sim uf$.

(C) If e is the LUB of orthogonal projections $\{e_i\}$, and $e \sim f$, then there exist orthogonal projections $\{f_i\}$ with LUB f satisfying $e_i \sim f_i$ for all i.

(D) If $e_1, \ldots, e_n$ are orthogonal projections with sum e, $f_1, \ldots, f_n$ orthogonal projections with sum f, and $e_i \sim f_i$ for all i, then $e \sim f$.

(E) If projections e, f satisfy $eAf \neq 0$ then there

41

exist non-zero projections e_1, f_1 with $e_1 \leq e$, $f_1 \leq f$,
$e_1 \sim f_1$.

(F) If $\{e_i\}$ are orthogonal projections with LUB e, $\{f_i\}$ orthogonal projections with LUB f, $ef = 0$, and $e_i \sim f_i$ for all i then $e \sim f$.

Discussion of the axioms. (A, B). These are trivially verified by both equivalence and *-equivalence. But it is worth noting that at the moment axiom B is invoked, we decisively part company with the rather similar enterprise of Maharam [12].

Axiom B cannot be proved from the remaining ones: let the ring be the direct sum of two fields and let $\sim$ interchange the two projections.

(C). For *-equivalence see Theorem 24. For ordinary equivalence we need an argument straightening idempotents into projections.

THEOREM 28. Ordinary equivalence in a Baer *-ring satisfies axiom C.

Proof. Let the equivalence of e, f be implemented by x, y. Well-order the index set for the e's; we now write $\{e_\alpha\}$, systematically using Greek letters for ordinals. For any α let g_α be the LUB of all e_β with $\beta < \alpha$. Then the g's are a well-ordered ascending set of projections with LUB e. Let h_α be the right projection of the idempotent $yg_\alpha x$. We take f_α to be $h_{\alpha+1} - h_\alpha$. The projection $e_\alpha = g_{\alpha+1} - g_\alpha$ is equivalent to the idempotent $yg_{\alpha+1}x - yg_\alpha x$ (Theorem 15), and the latter is equivalent to f_α (Theorem 18). It is clear that the f_α's are orthogonal and have LUB f.

Up to §9 a weaker axiom than C will actually be used.

(C') If $e = e_1 + e_2$ with e_1, e_2 orthogonal, and $e \sim f$, then there exist orthogonal projections f_1, f_2 with $f = f_1 + f_2$, $e_1 \sim f_1$, $e_2 \sim f_2$.

It is conceivable that axiom C is provable from A, B, C', D, E, F.

(D). For ordinary equivalence, see Theorem 17. For *-equivalence, see Theorem 25.

(E) With the interpretation of *-equivalence, axiom E need not hold in a Baer *-ring; the projections given in exercise 10, §3 furnish a counter-example.

With the interpretation of ordinary equivalence, it is not known whether (E) holds. It is valid in a *-regular ring: take $x \neq 0$ in eAf and take e_1, f_1 to be the left and right projections of x (exercise 7, §3).

Before discussing axiom F we make a simple remark about central decomposition. Let A be a Baer *-ring. Let $\{u_i\}$ be central orthogonal projections in A, with LUB 1. The mapping $x \rightarrow \{xu_i\}$ is manifestly an isomorphism of A into the complete direct sum of the rings $u_i A$. While this mapping need not at all be onto we do get all the projections of the complete direct sum: just take the LUB of the components.

(F). This axiom does hold for *-equivalence. We prove this by establishing a criterion for *-equivalence in terms of the existence of a "bisecting" projection.

THEOREM 29. Let e, f be orthogonal projections in a Baer *-ring. Then $e \overset{*}{\sim} f$ if and only if there exists a projection g satisfying 2ege = e, 2fgf = f, 2geg = 2gfg = g.

Proof. Suppose such a g exists. Define $x = 2egf$. Then

$x^* = 2fge$, $xx^* = 4egfge = 2ege = e$, $x^*x = 4fgegf = 2fgf = f$.

Conversely, suppose e and f are *-equivalent via x. The element g can be exhibited as a matrix. We can assume $e + f = 1$ harmlessly, and then A is a 2 by 2 *-matrix ring, with

$$e = \begin{pmatrix} 1 & 0 \\ 0 & 0 \end{pmatrix}, \quad f = \begin{pmatrix} 0 & 0 \\ 0 & 1 \end{pmatrix}, \quad x = \begin{pmatrix} 0 & 1 \\ 0 & 0 \end{pmatrix}.$$

We take

$$2g = \begin{pmatrix} 1 & 1 \\ 1 & 1 \end{pmatrix};$$

for the invertibility of 2 see exercises 11 and 12 of §3.

For the reader who prefers to avoid matrices, we give an alternate direct argument. Let g be the right projection of $e + x$. Then

$$(e + x)g = e + x. \tag{1}$$

Now $(1 - g)$ is the right-annihilating projection of $e + x$. We have $(e + x)(e - x^*) = 0$, therefore $e - x^* \in (1 - g)A$, therefore

$$g(e - x^*) = 0. \tag{2}$$

In the same way, since $e + x$ is right-annihilated by $x - f$ (note that $x^2 = 0$) and by $1 - e - f$, we have

$$g(x - f) = 0, \tag{3}$$

$$g(1 - e - f) = 0. \tag{4}$$

Take $*$ in (2), getting $xg = eg$. Substitute eg for xg in (1):

$$2eg = e + x. \tag{5}$$

Right-multiplication of (5) by e yields $2ege = e$. Left-multiplication by g and use of (3) and (4) yields $2geg = g$. Next we substitute xg for eg in (1) and left-multiply by x^*. We get

$$2fg = x^* + f. \tag{6}$$

Right-multiplication of (6) by f yields $2fgf = f$; left-multiplication by g and use of (2) and (4) yields $2gfg = g$.

THEOREM 30.   Under $*$-equivalence, Baer $*$-rings satisfy axiom F.

Proof. Set $u_i = e_i + f_i$. Let T be the subring of A commuting with all the u's. By Theorem 20, T is a Baer
*-subring of A. Manifestly the u's are central in T. The
e's, f's and partial isometries linking them are easily seen
to lie in T. Our problem has thus been completely transferred to T. But here the properties of central decomposition (see the remark above), plus the characterization in
Theorem 29, make the result immediate.

I do not know whether axiom F holds for ordinary
equivalence in a Baer *-ring. For regular Baer *-rings,
however, axiom F is true. This was proved in [8]; in the
exercises below we outline a slightly different way of doing
it.

Summary. Baer *-rings under *-equivalence satisfy A, B,
C, D, F; they do not necessarily satisfy E. Baer *-rings
under ordinary equivalence satisfy A, B, C, D; the status of
E and F is not known. Regular Baer *-rings under ordinary
equivalence satisfy all the axioms A to F; in addition the
main theorem in [8] proves them to be finite (for a purely
lattice-theoretic proof and extensive discussion see [1]).

EXERCISES. 1.(a) Let e, f be projections in a ring A with involution. Assume that the right annihilator of $e(1 - f)$ is generated by a projection $1 - g$. Prove that e, f have a LUB (in the partially ordered set of projections in A) and that $g = (e \cup f) - f$.

(b) Make a similar discussion for the left annihilator of $e(1 - f)$, leading to $e - (e \cap f)$.

2. If e, f are projections in a *-regular ring, prove that $(e \cup f) - f \sim e - (e \cap f)$. (Use exercise 1, and exercise 7 of §3.)

3. Prove: if two projections in a *-regular ring have a common complement they are equivalent. (Apply exercise 2.)

4. In a ring A with involution *, suppose the projection e is equivalent to $f = 1 - e$ via x, y. Assume that the right annihilator of $e + x$ is generated by a projection $1 - g$. Prove that $e \cap g$ and $f \cap g$ exist and $= 0$, and that $e \cup g$ and $f \cup g$ exist and $= 1$. (Hint: (a) Suppose a projection h is given with $h \geq e$ and g. Right-multiply (1) by h. Get $x = xh$, $f = fh$, $h = 1$. (b) $h \geq f$ and g. Get $x = xh$ and use (1) to work back to $h \geq e$. (c) $h \leq e$ and g. Instead of

(2) we have $g(e - y) = 0$. Left-multiply by h: $h = hy = hey$

$= 0$. (d) $h \leq f$ and g. Left-multiply (3) by h: $h = hx = hfx$

$= 0$.)

     5. Prove: two orthogonal projections in a *-regular

ring are equivalent if and only if they have a common com-

plement. (Can reduce to the case where the projections add

up to 1. Use exercises 3 and 4.)

     6. Show that axiom F holds in a regular Baer *-ring.

(Introduce u_i's as in Theorem 30, make them central.

Argue that the criterion in exercise 5 is preserved under

LUB's. Comment: we are coming dangerously close to

making the project a piece of lattice theory.)

5. ORTHOGONAL COMPARABILITY

From now till the end of §12 we shall work with a Baer *-ring A having an equivalence relation for which the six axioms (A-F) of §4 are assumed. For brevity, this hypothesis will not be repeated in the statements of the theorems and exercises, but we shall remind the reader at the beginning of each section. We state explicitly at this point: axioms A-F are tacitly assumed in the theorems and exercises of §§5-9 (except Theorem 39, exercise 2 in §7, and exercise 2 in §8).

One main objective is this: we have assumed orthogonal additivity of equivalence outright (axiom F) and mean to prove it without the assumption that e and f are orthogonal. On the road to this goal we develop a certain amount of structure theory, of interest in its own right.

A similar situation exists for comparability. In this section we easily get it in the orthogonal case, and in the end we shall have it unrestrictedly.

We begin by proving four simple results, which need proof now since all we know about equivalence comes from the postulates.

THEOREM 31.   Equivalent projections have equal central covers.

Proof. Assume $e \sim f$. If u is a central projection annihilating e then $0 = ue$ and $ue \sim uf$ by axiom B. By axiom A, $uf = 0$. Thus e and f are annihilated by exactly the same central projections and therefore have the same central cover.

THEOREM 32.   If $e \sim f$ and e is finite, then f is finite.

Proof. Let $f \sim h$ with $h \leq f$; we must prove $h = f$. By axiom C', there exists $g \leq e$ with $g \sim h$, $e - g \sim f - h$. Then $g \sim h \sim f \sim e$, whence $g = e$ since e is finite. By axiom A,

$f - h = 0$.

THEOREM 33. Any abelian projection is finite.

Proof. Let e be abelian, $f \leq e$, $e \sim f$. By Theorem 22d,

$f = ue$, u central. By axiom B, $(1 - u)e \sim (1 - u)f = 0$. By

axiom A, $(1 - u)e = 0$, whence $e = ue = f$.

THEOREM 34. If e is abelian and $e \sim f$ then f is abelian.

Proof. It will suffice to prove that any projection $h \leq f$ has

the form $h = uf$ with u central. By axiom C', $h \sim g$ with

$g \leq e$. By Theorem 22d, $g = ue$ with $u = C(g)$. By Theorem

31, $C(g) = C(h) = u$. Thus $h \leq u$ as well as $h \leq f$, and so

$h \leq uf$. By axiom B, $ue \sim uf$ and so $h \sim uf$. By Theorems

32 and 33, f is finite and so is uf. Hence $h = uf$.

We write $e \overset{<}{\sim} f$ if $e \sim f_1$ with $f_1 < f$; $\overset{>}{\sim}$ has the

obvious opposite meaning.

THEOREM 35. If e, f are orthogonal projections there

exists a central projection u such that $ue \overset{<}{\sim} uf$, $(1 - u)e$

$\overset{<}{\sim} (1 - u)f$.

Proof. Consider sets $\{e_i\}, \{f_i\}$ of orthogonal projections with $e_i \leq e$, $f_i \leq f$, $e_i \sim f_i$. By Zorn's lemma we can assume the setup to be maximal, and for such a maximal choice let g be the LUB of $\{e_i\}$, h the LUB of $\{f_i\}$. We have $g \sim h$ by axiom F. Write $k = e - g$, $m = f - h$. If $kAm \neq 0$, it follows from axiom E that the sets $\{e_i\}, \{f_i\}$ can be enlarged. Thus $kAm = 0$, from which we deduce that the central covers of k and m are orthogonal (Theorem 22b). The element $C(m)$ will do for u. For $(1 - u)m = 0$ by the definition of $C(m)$. Also $uk = 0$ since $C(k)u = 0$ and $C(k)k = k$. Since $k = e - g$, $uk = 0$ leads to $ue = ug$; and from $h \leq f$ we get $uh \leq uf$. From $g \sim h$ we get $ug \sim uh$ by axiom B. Together we have $ue = ug \sim uh \leq uf$ so that $ue \lesssim uf$. In the same way $(1 - u)e \gtrsim (1 - u)f$.

We are able at this point to prove a result on the uniqueness of subtraction which we shall use later. In due course (§12, exercise 2) we will get this in a suitably strengthened form.

THEOREM 36. Suppose e is finite and $e \lesssim 1 - e$. Assume $f, g \leq e$ and $f \sim g$. Then $e - f \sim e - g$.

Proof. The equivalence between e and a portion of 1 - e induces (by axiom C') an equivalence between e - f and a projection h orthogonal to e. A fortiori, h is orthogonal to e - g. We apply Theorem 35 to h and e - g. We may put the matter as follows: after dropping down to a direct summand and changing notation we may assume $h \precsim e - g$ or $e - g \precsim h$. Since $h \sim e - f$, this gives, respectively $e - f \precsim e - g$ or $e - g \precsim e - f$ (in the second case axiom C' is used again in switching from h to e - f). If we do not actually get equivalence, then on adding the equivalent projections f and g we contradict the finiteness of e.

EXERCISES. 1. Prove that A is a factor (i.e. the only central projections are 0, 1) if and only if any two projections are comparable: either $e \precsim f$ or $f \precsim e$.

2. Prove: if e is finite and $f \leq e$, then f is finite.

3. Suppose the projection e is not central. Prove that there exists a projection f with $e \sim f$ and f incomparable with e, i.e. neither $f \geq e$ nor $f \leq e$ holds. (Hint: $eA(1 - e) \neq 0$. Get g, h non-zero, equivalent, under

e, 1 - e.   Take f = h + e - g.)

4.   Prove the following equivalent: (a) e is central,

(b) e ~ f implies f ≤ e.   (Compare exercise 8 in §2.   For

(b) implies (a), use exercise 3.   Maharam [12] calls this

property "invariance".)

6. THE SCHRÖDER-BERNSTEIN THEOREM

Axioms A-F are in force except in Theorem 39.

We first prove a theorem (to be used again later) which serves as a nice prelude to the Schröder-Bernstein theorem. (Compare exercise 2, §2 for the non-* version.)

THEOREM 37. An infinite ring contains an infinite set of orthogonal equivalent non-zero projections. (We note again that in the present context the notion of infinite is not intrinsic to the ring, but depends on the postulated equivalence relation.)

Proof. We have $1 \sim e_1 \neq 1$. Write $f_1 = 1 - e_1$. By axiom C' we write e_1 as the orthogonal sum of e_2, f_2 with

$e_1 \sim e_2$, $f_1 \sim f_2$; then we write e_2 as the orthogonal sum

of e_3, f_3 with $e_2 \sim e_3$, $f_2 \sim f_3$, etc. The f's are the de-

sired set; they are all non-zero by axiom A.

Next we need a preliminary result.

THEOREM 38. Let $\{e_i\}$ be orthogonal equivalent projec-

tions indexed by a set I. Let J be a subset of I with the

same cardinal number as I. Let $f = \text{LUB} \{e_i, i \epsilon I\}$,

$g = \text{LUB} \{e_j, j \epsilon J\}$. Then $f \sim g$.

Proof. We cannot apply axiom F at once, lacking the re-

quisite orthogonality of f and g. But this is easily

remedied. Divide J into two subsets J_1 and J_2, both with

the same given cardinal number, and note that $I - J_1$ also

has this cardinal. Write h_1, h_2, h_3 for the LUB's of the

e's taken over the sets J_1, J_2, and $I-J_1$. Since the sets J_1

and J_2 are disjoint and have the same cardinal we have

$h_1 \sim h_2$ by axiom F; likewise $h_1 \sim h_3$. Since f is the

orthogonal sum of h_1 and h_3, g the orthogonal sum of

h_1 and h_2, we can conclude $f \sim g$ from axiom D.

We insert at this point a needed elementary result on projections in Baer *-rings.

THEOREM 39.   Let $e_1 \geq e_2 \geq e_3 \ldots$ be a descending sequence of projections in a Baer *-ring. Let f denote the LUB of $\{e_i - e_{i+1}\}$ and g the GLB of $\{e_i\}$. Then f and g are orthogonal and $e_1 = f + g$.

Proof. We note that g is orthogonal to each $e_i - e_{i+1}$ and hence to f. Moreover $g \leq e_1$ and $e_i - e_{i+1} \leq e_i \leq e_1$, so $e_1 \geq f + g$. $e_1 - e_n$ is the orthogonal sum of $e_1 - e_2$, $e_2 - e_3, \ldots, e_{n-1} - e_n$. Hence $e_1 - e_n \leq f$, and $e_n \geq e_1 - f$. This being true for all n, we have $g \geq e_1 - f$. Hence $e_1 = f + g$.

The proof of the Schröder-Bernstein theorem is in essence the usual one of set theory. For clarity we first formulate it in a different way.

THEOREM 40. Suppose e_o is an orthogonal direct sum of e_1, f_1, g_1 and $e_o \sim e_1$. Then $e_o \sim e_1 + f_1$.

Proof. We write

$$e_o = e_1 + f_1 + g_1 \,,$$

$$e_1 = e_2 + f_2 + g_2 \,,$$

$$e_2 = e_3 + f_3 + g_3 \,,$$

$$\cdots$$

Here the projections in each column are all equivalent, and each equation represents an orthogonal decomposition obtained from the preceding equation by two applications of axiom C. Note that the f's and g's are all mutually orthogonal. We have $e_o \geq e_1 \geq e_2 \geq \cdots$. Let h be the GLB of the e's. By Theorem 39, e_o is the LUB of the orthogonal projections h, $\{e_i - e_{i+1} \,, i = 0, 1, \ldots \}$; alternatively we have that e_o is the LUB of h and all the f's and g's. In just the same way, e_1 is the LUB of h and the f's and g's starting at i = 2. On comparing e_o and $e_1 + f_1$, we thus see that the difference between them is that one g got chopped out of e_o. Now by Theorem 38, the LUB of $\{g_1, g_2, g_3 \cdots \}$ is equivalent to the LUB of $\{g_2, g_3, g_4 \cdots \}$. We match off the remaining pieces identically and conclude $e_o \sim e_1 + f_1$.

THEOREM 41. $e \overset{<}{\sim} f$ and $f \overset{<}{\sim} e$ imply $e \sim f$.

Proof. Write $e \sim h \leq f$, $f \sim k \leq e$. We use axiom C' to move the orthogonal decomposition $f = h + (f - h)$ over to k, getting (say) $k = e_1 + f_1$. If we set $e_0 = e$, $g_1 = e - k$ we have the exact setup of Theorem 40. The conclusion $e_0 \sim e_1 + f_1$ is the same as $e \sim f$.

Remarks. 1. Theorem 41 will not be used until we prove Theorem 63 in §14, and there it could be avoided. However, as a matter of exposition, it seems reasonable to place it early in the sequence of theorems.

2. A. Lebow [Proc. Amer. Math. Soc. 19(1968), 144-5] has given a neat arrangement of a proof of the Schröder-Bernstein theorem via the fixed point theorem for monotone maps on complete lattices. His proof works for actual *-equivalence in any *-ring in which the lattice of projections is complete.

EXERCISES. 1. Use the relation $e \overset{<}{\sim} f$ to define a relation on equivalence classes of projections. Prove that it is a partial ordering.

2.   Prove that the partial ordering of exercise 1 is a linear ordering if and only if the ring is a factor.

3.   Prove that the partially ordered set of exercise 1 is a distributive lattice. (Use Theorem 35 to perform central decompositions until the three given projections are comparable in each summand.)

4.   Observe that it is meaningful to speak of a finite or infinite equivalence class (exercise 2 of §5). Prove that the infinite equivalence classes in a factor form a well ordered set. (Hint: study the cardinal numbers that arise in writing a projection e as the LUB of orthogonal projections all equivalent to a projection f (which might be e itself).)

For more information on equivalence classes of projections, from the point of view of cardinal algebras, see Fillmore [2].

5.   Prove: a finite ring cannot contain an infinite set of equivalent orthogonal non-zero projections (use Theorem 38).

7. INFINITE RINGS

Axioms A-F are in force except in exercise 2.

On the way to Theorem 44 we prove two preliminary theorems. The first is a variant of Theorem 38.

THEOREM 42. Let $\{e_i\}$ be a set of $\aleph$ equivalent orthogonal projections ($\aleph$ infinite) with LUB e, and suppose $fe = 0$, $f \lesssim e_1$, Then $e + f$ is the LUB of $\aleph$ orthogonal projections each equivalent to e_1.

Proof. We have $e_1 = f_1 + g_1$ orthogonally with $f_1 \sim f$. By axiom C' we move this to $e_i = f_i + g_i$, $f_i \sim f_1$, $g_i \sim g_1$. The set $\{g_i\}$ can be paired with the set $\{f_i, f\}$, since adding 1 to an infinite cardinal leaves it unchanged. Let h_i

63

be the sum of g_i and the f_j or f going with it.   Then

$h_i \sim e_1$ (axiom D), and plainly $e + f$ is the LUB of $\{h_i\}$.

THEOREM 43. Suppose $\{e_i\}$ is a maximal set of ortho-

gonal equivalent projections, say with cardinal number $\aleph$

($\aleph$ infinite).   Then there exists a non-zero central pro-

jection u such that u is the LUB of $\aleph$ orthogonal

projections equivalent to ue_1 .

Proof. Write e for the LUB of $\{e_i\}$.   We apply the com-

parability theorem (Theorem 35) to e_1 and $1 - e$.   It can-

not be the case that $e_1 \precsim 1 - e$; for then we could adjoin to

$\{e_i\}$ the equivalent projection inside $1 - e$, contradicting

the assumed maximality.   Hence there exists a non-zero

central projection u with $u(1 - e) \precsim ue_1$.   Now u is the

LUB of $u(1 - e)$ and $\{ue_i\}$; moreover all ue_i are equivalent

by axiom B.   We quote Theorem 42.

THEOREM 44. In a purely infinite ring 1 can be exhibited

as the LUB of $\aleph_0$ equivalent orthogonal projections.

Proof. By Theorem 37 the ring contains an infinite family

of equivalent orthogonal non-zero projections $\{e_i\}$ which

we can suppose, by Zorn's lemma, to be maximal. We

apply Theorem 43. The result is a non-zero central pro-

jection u such that u is the LUB of an infinite number of

equivalent orthogonal projections. Divide these into $\aleph_0$

subsets of equal cardinal; this results in u being the LUB

of $\aleph_0$ equivalent orthogonal projections. Since the given

ring A is purely infinite we can repeat the construction in

the complementary summand $(1 - u)A$, and we continue the

argument ad transfinitum.

THEOREM 45. In a purely infinite ring there exists a pro-

jection e with $1 \sim e \sim 1 - e$.

Proof. Split the projections given by Theorem 44 into two

equal halves and apply Theorem 38.

EXERCISES. 1. (a) In a purely infinite ring show that for

any n, $1 = e_1 + \ldots + e_n$ with the e's orthogonal projections

all equivalent to 1.

(b) In a purely infinite ring show that 1 is the LUB

of $\aleph_0$ orthogonal projections all equivalent to 1.

  2. In this exercise equivalence for the moment becomes "concrete."

  (a) Let A be a Baer *-ring which is purely infinite relative to *-equivalence. Assume axiom E satisfied (and hence all of A-F). Let A_n denote the n by n matrix ring over A, endowed with the natural involution (*-transposition). Prove that A and A_n are *-isomorphic.

  (b) Let A be a Baer *-ring which is purely infinite relative to ordinary equivalence. Assume axioms E, F. Let A_n be the n by n matrix ring over A. Prove that A and A_n are isomorphic.

8. TYPE I

The following theorem exhibits a central decomposition of a type I ring into summands that are homogeneous in an appropriate sense.

THEOREM 46. Let e be a non-zero abelian projection. Then there exists a non-zero central projection u which is the LUB of orthogonal projections all equivalent to ue.

Proof. Let $e_1 = e$ and let $\{e_i\}$ be a maximal set of orthogonal equivalent projections, say with LUB f. (Note: if the number of e_i's is infinite, we could simply quote Theorem 43. The point is that even in the finite case the abelian character of e allows us to smooth out the ragged edge.)

67

By maximality we cannot have $e \precsim 1 - f$. We apply comparability (Theorem 35) to the orthogonal projections e and $1 - f$. After dropping down to a direct summand we may assume $1 - f \precsim e$. Now if $f = 1$, we are done since then $1 = $ LUB of $\{e_i\}$. Assume $f \neq 1$. Then if $1 - f \sim k \leq e$ we have $k = ue$ with u a non-zero central projection (Theorem 22d). Then u is the LUB of the orthogonal equivalent projections $\{ue_i, 1 - f\}$.

We proceed to Theorem 48 which will be used in §§10, 11 in proving additivity of equivalence for finite rings of Type I. First a preliminary theorem.

Theorem 47. Let A be a finite ring and suppose 1 is a sum $e_1 + \ldots + e_n$ of orthogonal equivalent abelian projecttions. Then any set of equivalent orthogonal non-zero projections in A has at most n members.

Proof. Suppose on the contrary that $f_1, \ldots, f_{n+1}$ are non-zero, orthogonal, and equivalent. Necessarily e_1 is faithful; hence $e_1 A f_1 \neq 0$ since the vanishing of $e_1 A f_1$ would entail $f_1 = 0$. By axiom E we have non-zero projections

$g \leq e_1$, $h_1 \leq f_1$ with $g \sim h_1$. By axiom C' the projection h_1 may be copied inside each of $f_2, \ldots, f_{n+1}$, yielding projections $h_2, \ldots, h_{n+1}$ equivalent to h_1. By Theorem 22d, $g = ue_1$ with u central. Then on the one hand the projection u is the orthogonal sum of $ue_1, \ldots, ue_n$, and on the other hand uA contains the orthogonal projections $h_1, \ldots, h_{n+1}$, all equivalent to ue_1. This contradicts the finiteness of u.

THEOREM 48. Let A be a finite ring of type I, $\{e_i\}$ a set of orthogonal projections in A. Then there exists a non-zero central projection u such that all but a finite number of $\{ue_i\}$ vanish.

Proof. We begin by applying Theorem 46. After dropping to a direct summand and changing notation we have that 1 is an orthogonal sum of n orthogonal equivalent abelian projections (note that all the projections obtained are abelian by Theorem 34, and that n is necessarily finite by the finiteness of A). Choose equivalent non-zero abelian projections f_i such that, the e's being appropriately numbered, we have $f_1 \le e_1, \ldots, f_k \le e_k$ with k as large as possible; by Theorem 47, $k \le n$. For any e_j other than $e_1, \ldots, e_k$ we must have $f_1 A e_j = 0$; otherwise by appropriate use of axioms E and C' we could arrange a setup as above with $k + 1$ instead of k. We take for u the central cover $C(f_1)$ of f_1; since $f_1 A e_j = 0$ implies $C(f_1)C(e_j) = 0$ (Theorem 22b) we have $ue_j = 0$ as required.

At the other extreme the assumption of no abelian projections (i. e. no type I summand) allows all projections to be cut in half.

THEOREM 49. Let A be a ring with no abelian projections other than 0, and e a projection in A. Then e can be written $e = f + g$, with f and g equivalent orthogonal projections.

Proof. Consider sets of projections $\{f_i\}, \{g_i\}$, all mutually orthogonal, all $\le e$, and with $f_i \sim g_i$. Choose the setup to be maximal (Zorn) and let f, g be the respective LUB's. Then f and g are orthogonal, and they are equivalent by axiom F. Write $h = e - f - g$. We have to prove $h = 0$.

Suppose the contrary, and observe that by hypothesis h is

not an abelian projection. Therefore there exists a projec-

tion $k \leq h$, not central in hAh. From this $kA(h-k) \neq 0$.

For suppose it is 0. Then (take *) $(h-k)Ak = 0$. It follows

that for any x in A, $kxh = kxk$ and $hxk = kxk$. Thus

$kxh = hxk$ and $k(hxh) = (hxh)k$, contradicting the fact that k

is not central in hAh. So $kA(h-k) \neq 0$. By axiom E we can

find non-zero equivalent projections contained in k and h-k,

and these may be used to enlarge $\{f_i\}$ and $\{g_i\}$, a con-

tradiction.

EXERCISES. 1. Generalize Theorem 49 by showing that

e can be divided into n equivalent orthogonal pieces for

any integer n.

   2. We revert to a Baer *-ring A under actual

*-equivalence. Assume axiom E (and thus all of A-F).

Assume further that A has no I_{fin} summand. Prove that

A is an algebra over the field of rational numbers. (Use

exercise 12 in §3.)

9. ADDITIVITY OF EQUIVALENCE IN THE PURELY INFINITE CASE

Axioms A-F are in force.

We are ready to prove additivity of equivalence in the purely infinite case. It may seem paradoxical that for this problem the infinite case is easier than the finite; however this is a subject where room to "push projections around" is valuable.

THEOREM 50. In a purely infinite ring let $\{e_i\}$ be orthogonal projections with LUB e, $\{f_i\}$ orthogonal projections with LUB f, and suppose $e_i \sim f_i$ for every i. Then $e \sim f$.

Proof. By Theorem 45 we have a projection g satisfying $1 \sim g \sim 1 - g$. By axiom C (used in full for the first time)

73

we can move $\{e_i\}$ and e under g, $\{f_i\}$ and f under

$1 - g$. Now axiom F can be applied.

10. THE POSTULATE OF CENTRAL ADDITIVITY

On the basis of axioms A-F we are unable to complete the proof of additivity of equivalence (but we note that no examples are at hand to show that it cannot be done).

We shall continue the discussion in axiomatic style, introducing a new axiom G in this section, and an alternate axiom H in the next.

(G) Let $\{u_i\}$ be orthogonal central projections. Let e_i, f_i be projections in $u_i A$, and let e, f be the LUB of $\{e_i\}, \{f_i\}$ respectively. Suppose $e_i \sim f_i$ for all i. Then $e \sim f$.

It is immediate (from the strong properties of a central decomposition in an AW^*-algebra) that axiom G holds holds in AW^*-algebras. So for that application, the axiom is entirely acceptable.

Note that with axiom G at hand, Theorem 48 suffices to settle additivity of equivalence in the I_{fin} case. This is what I had in mind when I wrote, on the third and fourth last lines of page 533 of [8], "This suffices to prove unrestricted additivity of equivalence in the type I case". However, central additivity was at that point in [8] not yet available, so there was a gap in the argument. (The same oversight occurs in Skornyakov's book [15]). We shall repair the oversight in the next section.

(We note parenthetically that the next sentence in [8], concerning the continuity axioms, is sound, and so the main theorem of [8] is actually not affected.)

If we wish to finish our project on the basis of axiom G, it remains to handle the II_1 case. This can be done by proving Lemma 4.14 of [5], extended to any cardinal number.

(Let me record the reason [5, Lemma 4.14] was proved only in the countable case. I then regarded Theorem 5.2 of [5] -- the equivalence of left and right projections -- as a principal target, and I was aware that in AW^*-algebras

countable additivity was good enough for proving Theorem
5.2.)

THEOREM 5.   Let   A   be a Baer *-ring with an equivalence
relation satisfying axioms A-F.   Assume that   A   is finite
relative to the equivalence relation.   Let $\{e_\alpha\}$ be a well-
ordered collection of orthogonal projections in A with LUB
e.   For every α let $g_\alpha = \text{LUB}\{e_\beta,\ \beta < \alpha\}$.   Assume
$e \lesssim 1 - e$ and $e_1 \neq 0$.   Then it cannot be the case that
$g_\alpha \lesssim e - g_\alpha$ for all α.

Proof.   We suppose the contrary and derive a contradiction.

In view of the assumption $e \lesssim 1 - e$ and axiom C',
we can find a projection k   inside $1 - e$, $k \sim e - e_1$.   The
idea of the proof is to build stepwise a replica of   e   inside
k   and thus contradict finiteness.

We shall construct certain projections $f_\alpha, h_\alpha \leq k$.
Observe that our notation for the e's and   g's   is such that
$g_1 = 0$, $g_2 = e_1$, $g_3 = e_1 + e_2$,   etc.   For $\alpha \geq 2$ we have
$g_\alpha \lesssim e - g_\alpha \leq e - e_1 \sim k$.   Thus $e_1 = g_2 \lesssim k$, and there
is a replica of e_1 inside k.   This is our choice for f_1, and

we take $h_1 = 0$. Suppose f_α, h_α have been selected for

$\alpha < \lambda$ satisfying: $f_\alpha, h_\alpha \leq k$, $\{f_\alpha\}$ orthogonal, $f_\alpha = h_{\alpha+1} - h_\alpha$,

h_α = LUB of preceding h's for α a limit ordinal, $e_\alpha \sim f_\alpha$,

$g_\alpha \sim h_\alpha$. If λ is a limit ordinal we take $h_\lambda = \text{LUB} \{h_\alpha,$

$\alpha < \lambda\}$. If λ is not a limit ordinal we take $h_\lambda = h_{\lambda-1} + f_{\lambda-1}$.

In either case $g_\lambda \sim h_\lambda$ (axiom F is used in the limiting

case). We define f_λ as follows. We have $g_{\lambda+1} \lesssim e - g_{\lambda+1}$

$\leq e - e_1 \sim k$. In this equivalence of $g_{\lambda+1}$ with a portion of

k, g_λ corresponds say to k' (axiom C'). Then

$e_\lambda = g_{\lambda+1} - g_\lambda \lesssim k - k$. We have $k' \sim g_\lambda \sim h_\lambda$. By

Theorem 36 (applicable since $k \sim e - e_1 < e \leq 1 - k$),

$k - k' \sim k - h_\lambda$. Thus $e_\lambda \lesssim k - h_\lambda$, and we may choose for

f_λ a projection which is inside k, orthogonal to h_λ, and

equivalent to e_λ. With these choices of h_λ, f_λ we continue

to satisfy the requirements listed above.

Define f to be the LUB of all the f's thus con-

structed. We have $e \sim f \leq k \sim e - e_1$, a contradiction of

finiteness.

THEOREM 52. Let A be a Baer *-ring with an equivalence

relation satisfying axioms A-G. Then unrestricted additivity

holds: if $\{e_i\}$ are orthogonal projections with LUB e,
$\{f_i\}$ orthogonal projections with LUB f, $e_i \sim f_i$ for all i,
then $e \sim f$.

Proof. We have handled the purely infinite case (Theorem
50), and we have noted that Theorem 48 and axiom G dis-
pose of the I_{fin} case. It remains to treat the II_1 case.

We begin by using Theorem 49 to split each e_i and
correspondingly each f_i "in half". It suffices to study one
of the halves thus created. After a change of notation, this
means we can assume $e \lesssim 1 - e$ and $f \lesssim 1 - f$.

Let the cardinal number of the index set be $\aleph$. We
make an induction on $\aleph$. Well order the e's and f's by the
initial ordinal of the cardinal $\aleph$; we now write $\{e_\alpha\}$ and
$\{f_\alpha\}$ for the sets.

Write g_α for LUB $\{e_\beta, \beta < \alpha\}$ and h_α for LUB
$\{f_\beta, \beta < \alpha\}$. By the induction assumption $g_\alpha \sim h_\alpha$.

We apply Theorem 51 (the hypothesis $e_1 \neq 0$ is of
course harmless). It tells us that after dropping down to a
direct summand and changing notation we have $e - g_\lambda \lesssim g_\lambda$
for a suitable λ. (Note that axiom G allows us to paste

these central summands together). Since $g_\lambda \sim h_\lambda$ and

$h_\lambda \leq f \lesssim 1 - f$ we get $e - g_\lambda \lesssim 1 - f$. We now use axiom

C to move the projections $\{e_\alpha, \ \alpha > \lambda\}$ and their LUB

$e - g_\lambda$ underneath $1 - f$. Here axiom F applies to yield

$e - g_\lambda \sim f - h_\lambda$. Add this to $g_\lambda \sim h_\lambda$ (axiom D) and we reach

$e \sim f$.

11. THE PARALLELOGRAM LAW

By the parallelogram law we mean:

(H) For any projections e and f we have

$(e \cup f) - f \sim e - (e \cap f)$.

Axiom H for ordinary equivalence holds in any
*-regular ring (§4, exercise 2). Its validity for *-equiva-
lence in suitable Baer *-rings that include AW^*-algebras
will be discussed in the next section.

In this section we shall show that axiom H leads to
unrestricted additivity of equivalence, and we go on from
there to the additivity of finiteness.

THEOREM 53. Let A be a Baer *-ring with an equivalence
relation satisfying axioms A-F and H. Let e and f be faith-

ful abelian projections in A (so that A is of type I).
Then $e \sim f$.

Proof. Of course $eAf \neq 0$. By axiom E we have $e_1 \sim f_1$
with $e_1 \leq e$, $f_1 \leq f$. By Theorem 22d, $e_1 = ue$ with u central. If we have a way of putting these summands together,
the proof will be finished. Of course axiom G will do, but
our present task is to do it with axiom H.

We next note that if e and f are orthogonal, axiom
F will give us the needed authority to combine summands.

By Theorem 22d, $e \cap f = ve$ with v central. In the
direct summand vA, the components of e and f are equal
so we can dismiss this summand. This means (after a
change of notation) that we can assume $e \cap f = 0$. Then
axiom H gives us $e \sim (e \cup f) - f = g$, say. Note that g
shares with e the property of being a faithful abelian projection. Since $gf = 0$, we have $g \sim f$ by the remark in the
preceding paragraph, and hence $e \sim f$.

THEOREM 54. Let A be a Baer *-ring with an equivalence
relation satisfying axioms A-F and H. Then unrestricted

additivity holds: if $\{e_i\}$ are orthogonal projections with LUB e, $\{f_i\}$ orthogonal projections with LUB f, $e_i \sim f_i$ for all i, then $e \sim f$.

Proof. Because of Theorem 50, we need only handle the II_1 and I_{inf} case.

II_1. By two successive applications of Theorem 49 we break each e_i into four equivalent orthogonal pieces and (axiom C) we make a corresponding decomposition of each f_i. After a change of notation, this means that we can assume that A contains four orthogonal projections equivalent to e, and also four orthogonal projections equivalent to f.

Write $g = (e \cup f) - f$. Since g and f are orthogonal, we can apply orthogonal comparability (Theorem 35) to them. After dropping down to a direct summand and changing notation as usual, this means that we may treat two cases.

Case I. $f \lesssim g$. By axiom H, $g \sim e - (e \cap f) \leq e$. Thus $f \lesssim e \lesssim 1 - e$. By axiom C we move the f_i's underneath $1 - e$ and then apply orthogonal additivity (axiom F).

Case II. $g \lesssim f$. Write $h = 1 - (e \cup f)$, and note that f and h are orthogonal. We claim that $f \lesssim h$. Otherwise

(Theorem 35) we can pass to a direct summand where

$h \lesssim f$. But then $1 = h + g + f$ is the union of three ortho-

gonal projections all $\lesssim f$, whereas it contains four ortho-

gonal projections equivalent to f; this contradicts finiteness.

Hence $f \lesssim h \leq 1 - e$, and this time we move the projections

f_i underneath $1 - e$.

I_{fin}. (Once again it seems paradoxical that I_{fin} --

which ought to be the easiest case of all -- gives us some

extra trouble.)

We make a number of normalizations. First, each

e_i can be split into abelian projections. We might there-

fore as well assume that all the e_i's and f_i's are abelian.

Second, we make use of Theorem 48. As a consequence we

may assume that we have a central decomposition of 1 into

$\{u_j\}$ such that in each $u_j A$ all but a finite number of the e_i's

and f_i's vanish; we may further suppose that each e_i lies

in one of the summands $u_j A$. Third, we decompose each

$u_j A$ according to the finite number of central covers of e_i's

occurring inside it; now we have in each $u_j A$ a finite num-

ber of faithful abelian projections. If we string together one

e_i from each $u_j A$ (that has any) we get an abelian projection with central cover v = LUB of these u_j's. Putting to-

gether f's in the same way gives us another abelian pro-

jection with central cover v.   By Theorem 53 these two

projections are equivalent, and we may put aside the pieces

of e and f thus obtained.   We repeat this procedure three

times.   The upshot is that the number of e_i's in each $u_j A$

has been made divisible by 4.   We can now repeat verbatim

the technique used in the II_1 half of the proof, and this con-

cludes the proof of Theorem 54.

THEOREM 55.   Let A be a Baer *-ring with an equivalence

relation satisfying axioms A-F and H.   Let e, f, g be pro-

jections with $ef = 0$, $g \leq e+f$, and write $h = e+f-g$.   Then

A may be split into two direct summands in which $g \underset{\sim}{\leq} e$

and $h \underset{\sim}{\leq} f$, respectively.

Proof. Since g and h are orthogonal, so are $g \cap f$ and

$h \cap e$.   We apply Theorem 35 and drop down to direct sum-

mands with the usual change of notation.

   Case I. $g \cap f \underset{\sim}{\leq} h \cap e$.   By axiom H,

$$g = (g \cap f) + [g - (g \cap f)] \underset{\sim}{\leq} (h \cap e) + [(g \cup f) - f].$$

The last two terms are orthogonal projections, both $\leq$ e.
Hence g $\lesssim$ e.

Case II.   h $\cap$ e $\gtrsim$ g $\cap$ f.   We have

$$h = (h \cap e) + [h - (h \cap e)] \lesssim (g \cap f) + [(h \cup e) - e],$$

and argue similarly that h $\lesssim$ f.

THEOREM 56.   Let A be a Baer *-ring with an equivalence
relation satisfying axioms A-F and H.   Let e, f be finite
projections in A.   Then e $\cup$ f is finite.

Proof.   We may assume e $\cup$ f = 1.   If 1 is infinite we may
assume (drop to a direct summand) that it is purely infinite.
Then (Theorem 45) there exists a projection g such that
1 $\sim$ g $\sim$ 1 - g.   By axiom H,

$$1 - e = (e \cup f) - e \sim f - (e \cap f) \leq f,$$

and so 1 - e is finite.   We apply Theorem 55, with f replaced by 1 - e, so that h = 1 - g.   The algebra splits into
two direct summands in which g $\lesssim$ e and 1 - g $\gtrsim$ 1 - e
respectively; but both of these statements are contradictory.

12. GENERAL COMPARABILITY

When general additivity is at hand, the orthogonality restriction can be removed from Theorem 35. So without any further ado we state:

THEOREM 57. Let A be a Baer *-ring with an equivalence relation satisfying axioms A-F and either G or H. Let e, f be projections in A. Then there exists a central projection u such that $eu \lesssim uf$, $(1 - u)e \gtrsim (1 - u)f$.

EXERCISES. (In these two exercises axioms A-F and G or H are in force.)

    1. (Uniqueness of bisection). If $1 = e_1 + e_2 = f_1 + f_2$, $e_1 \sim e_2$, $f_1 \sim f_2$, $e_1 e_2 = f_1 f_2 = 0$, prove $e_1 \sim f_1$. (Hint:

use comparability on e_1 and f_1. If e_1 is finite, equiva-

lence is forced. If e_1 is purely infinite it is equivalent to

1 anyway.)

   2. (Uniqueness of subtraction). If $e \sim f$ and e is

finite, prove $1 - e \sim 1 - f$. (Compare Theorem 36.)

13. THE EP AND SR AXIOMS

If we wish to apply our results to AW^*-algebras there is still a missing link. We can get general additivity via central additivity as in §10, but we want the parallelo-gram law (1) for its own sake, (2) for its applications, e.g. to the additivity of finiteness and the modular law.

We now follow the first edition of <u>Rings of Operators</u> in discussing two further axioms. To shorten the writing we abbreviate "commutes with everything that commutes with" to CC.

(EP) For any non-zero element x there exists a self-adjoint element y with y CC x^*x, and x^*xy^2 a non-zero projection. (Existence of projections).

(SR)   For any element x we can write $x^*x = y^2$ with y self-adjoint and y CC x^*x.   (Square root).

Let us note at once that in this section we are no longer unifying two similar projects: we will be talking solely about actual equivalence in Baer *-rings.   Furthermore (Theorem 27) the SR axiom identifies equivalence and *-equivalence, so that there can be no ambiguity.

Axioms A, B, C, D, F are all fulfilled.   We now note that EP implies axiom E.

THEOREM 58.   Let A be a Baer *-ring satisfying the EP axiom, and let e and f be projections with eAf $\neq$ 0.   Then there exist non-zero projections e_1, f_1 satisfying $e_1 \leq e$, $f_1 \leq f$, $e_1 \overset{*}{\approx} f_1$.

Proof.   Take $x \neq 0$ in eAf.   Take y as given by the EP axiom: $y CC xx^*$, $e_1 = xx^*y^2$ a non-zero projection.   Since ex = x we have $ee_1 = e_1$, $e_1 \leq e$.   Set w = yx.   Then $xx^* = yxx^*y = xx^*y^2 = e_1$.   Hence (Theorem 23) x^*x is a projection f_1 *-equivalent to e_1.   Since xf = x, we get $f_1 f = f_1$ and $f_1 \leq f$.

In the proof of Theorem 62 we shall make use of a commuting subring (compare Theorem 20) and so the following will be needed:

THEOREM 59. Let A be a Baer *-ring satisfying the EP and SR axioms. Let S be a self-adjoint subset of A and let B = S' be the commuting ring. Then B likewise satisfies the EP and SR axioms.

Proof. Take x ϵ B. Then also x^*x ϵ B. Construct the element y in A whose existence is assured by the EP or SR axioms. Then since S commuting ring of x^*x, and y CC x^*x, we have y ϵ S' = B. The statement y CC x^*x continues to hold a fortiori in B.

The following rather technical pair of theorems will also be used in proving Theorem 62.

THEOREM 60. Let A be a Baer *-ring satisfying the SR axiom. Let e and f be projections such that ef - fe is invertible. Then there exists a projection h satisfying $(2h - 1)e(2h - 1) = f$.

Proof. We note the identity

$$-(ef - fe)^2 = ef(1 - e)fe + (1 - e)fef(1 - e). \tag{7}$$

It follows that $ef(1 - e)fe$ is invertible in eAe. Let $x = ef(1 - e)$. Let y be an element provided by the SR axiom: $y^* = y$, $y^2 = xx^* = ef(1 - e)fe$, $y \, CC \, xx^*$. Then y commutes with e; also $0 = y^2(1 - e) = (1 - e)y \cdot y(1 - e)$ so that (Theorem 21), $(1 - e)y = 0$, $y \in eAe$. Thus y is invertible in eAe; let z be its inverse, and note that z is a self-adjoint element of eAe satisfying $ef(1 - e)fez^2 = e$. The element z inherits from y the property $z \, CC \, ef(1 - e)fe$. We summarize the properties of z:

$$z = z^*, \ z \in eAe, \ z \, CC \, ef(1 - e)fe,$$
$$ef(1 - e)fez^2 = e. \tag{8}$$

Since $ef(1 - e)fe = efe - (efe)^2$ we have that efe is regular in eAe (compare §2, exercise 6). In a way similar to the construction of y and z we find s, a square root of efe, and an inverse t of s. They satisfy

$$t = t^*, \ t \in eAe, \ t \, CC \, efe, \ efet^2 = e. \tag{9}$$

$$s = s^*, \quad s \in eAe, \quad s^2 = efe, \quad st = ts = e. \tag{10}$$

We define $u = zf(1 - e)$. We have $uu^* = e$ by (8).

Next: $u^*u = (1 - e)fz^2f(1 - e)$, $u^*ufe = (1 - e)fe$. From this

it follows that $u^*u - (1 - e)$ left annihilates $ef - fe$. Since

$ef - fe$ is invertible, $u^*u = 1 - e$. Thus $e \overset{*}{\sim} 1 - e$ via the

element u. The *-equivalence of e and $1 - e$ shows that

2 is invertible in A (see exercise 12 in §3).

We are ready to define h by the equation

$$2h - 1 = s - u^*su + tf(1 - e) + (1 - e)ft. \tag{11}$$

Since e right annihilates u and $1 - e$, we get

$$(2h - 1)e = s + (1 - e)ft,$$

and then

$$(2h - 1)e(2h - 1) = s^2 + (1 - e)fts + stf(1 - e)$$
$$+ (1 - e)ft^2f(1 - e). \tag{12}$$

By (10) the sum of the first three terms on the right of (12) is

equal to

$$efe + ef(1 - e) + (1 - e)fe. \tag{13}$$

Using $t^2 efe = e$ from (9), we next compute that $ft^2 f - f$

left annihilates $ef - fe$ and is therefore 0. Thus the last

term in (12) is $(1 - e)f(1 - e)$. Combining this with the terms

given in (13) we find

$$(2h - 1)e(2h - 1) = f , \qquad (14)$$

as required. It remains to prove that h is an idempotent.

For this it will suffice to show

$$(2h - 1)(1 - e)(2h - 1) = 1 - f . \qquad (15)$$

For if we add (14) and (15) we get $(2h - 1)^2 = 1$ whence

$h = h^2$ since 4 can be cancelled.

Since $(1 - e)$ right annihilates s and t, we get

from (11)

$$(2h - 1)(1 - e) = -u^* su + tf(1 - e)$$

and then

$$(2h - 1)(1 - e)(2h - 1) = u^* s^2 u - u^* suft - tfu^* su$$

$$+ tf(1 - e)ft . \qquad (16)$$

We proceed to analyze the terms on the right of (16). We

have

$$u^* suft = (1 - e)fz\, szf(1 - e)ft$$

$$= (1 - e)fz\, sz[ef(1 - e)fe]t \ , \tag{17}$$

since e may be harmlessly inserted to the right of z and

the left of t. Now t commutes with efe, by (9), therefore

with $ef(1 - e)fe = efe - (efe)^2$, therefore with z by (8). In

(17) we may therefore bring t adjacent to s. Then (10) and

(8) collapse (17) down to $(1 - e)fe$.

Next, $tf(1 - e)ft = tefet - t(efe)^2t = e - efe$ by (9).

We tackle the term $u^* s^2 u$. We have

$$u^* s^2 u = (1 - e)fzefezf(1 - e). \tag{18}$$

Since $z\ CC\ efe - (efe)^2$ we have that z commutes with efe

and so the two z's in (18) may be brought adjacent. Let us

right multiply (18) by $ef - fe$. Only the term $-fe$ survives

and we find, using (8),

$$u^* s^* u(ef - fe) = -(1 - e)fefe. \tag{19}$$

It is now straightforward to check that the right side

of (16), right-multiplied by $ef - fe$, coincides with

$(1 - f)(ef - fe)$. We have therefore proved (15), and with it we have finished the proof of Theorem 60.

THEOREM 61. Let e and f be projections in a Baer *-ring
such that ef - fe is invertible. Then e ~ f ~ 1 - e ~ 1 - f,
e ∩ f = 0, e ∪ f = 1, e - (e ∩ f) ~ (e ∪ f) - f.

Proof. We quote the equivalences of e, f, 1 - e, 1 - f from
exercise 6 in § 2. Let g = e ∪ f. Then ge = e, gf = f,
g(ef - fe) = ef - fe whence g = 1. Similarly if k = e ∩ f,
then ke = k, kf = k, k(ef - fe) = 0, k = 0. The final statement of the theorem is evident.

THEOREM 62. Let A be a Baer *-ring satisfying the EP
and SR axioms. Then axiom H, the parallelogram law,
holds in A: for any projections e, f we have

e - (e ∩ f) ~ (e ∪ f) - f.

Proof. From (7) we see that $(ef - fe)^2$ commutes with e
and (by symmetry) with f as well. Let B be the subring
commuting with $(ef - fe)^2$. By Theorems 20 and 59, B is
again a Baer *-ring with EP and SR axioms. We switch the
problem to B; this means that we can start all over with the

added knowledge that $(ef - fe)^2$ is central.

Let v be the central cover of $(ef - fe)^2$. In the summand $(1 - v)A$ we have that e and f commute, whence our conclusion (for $e \cap f = ef$, $e \cup f = e + f - ef$). We may thus assume that the central cover of $(ef - fe)^2$ is 1.

Apply the EP axiom to $x = ef - fe$. The resulting projection, say w, $CC\, x^2 = (ef - fe)^2$ and is therefore central. In the direct summand wA, $ef - fe$ is invertible, and so (Theorem 61) we have our conclusion there (note that the SR axiom converts the equivalences to *-equivalences).

It remains to assemble these "local" parallelogram laws to a global one. Central additivity will do it, and we might therefore proceed that way if the context is AW^*-algebras. (But note the following annoyance if we try to operate this way in Baer *-rings: central additivity in the original ring will perhaps not imply it in the commuting ring of $(ef - fe)^2$.)

Theorem 60 was prepared to be used at this moment. We have orthogonal central projections, say $\{w_i\}$, with LUB 1. In w_iA, the element $w_i(ef - fe)$ is invertible. Hence by Theorem 60 there exists a projection h_i in w_iA

satisfying $(2h_i - 1)w_i e(2h_i - 1) = w_i f$. Let h be the LUB of $\{h_i\}$. Then h satisfies $(2h - 1)e(2h - 1) = f$, and the element $e(2h - 1)$ implements an equivalence of e and f. Likewise all of e, f, 1 - e, 1 - f are equivalent. The statements $e \cap f = 0$, $e \cup f = 1$ hold in each $w_i A$ (Theorem 61) and therefore also in A. We have proved Theorem 62.

EXERCISES. 1. Prove that a ring with involution satisfying the EP axiom is a Zorn ring (see exercise 12 in §1 for Zorn rings).

2. Prove general comparability of projections by using the technique of Theorem 62 (in the notation of Theorem 62, e and f commute in the summand $(1 - v)A$ and orthogonal comparability applies. In the summand vA, e ~ f. This was the method used in the first edition of Rings of Operators).

14. EQUIVALENCE OF LEFT AND RIGHT PROJECTIONS

We repeat the remark that in this section (and in the next two as well) no unification is in progress; we deal explicitly with equivalence in Baer *-rings satisfying the EP and SR axioms.

THEOREM 63. Let x be any element in a Baer *-ring satisfying the EP and SR axioms. Let e be the right projection of x, f the left projection of x. Then $e \sim f$.

Proof. The idea of the proof is that the EP axiom gives us an equivalence between a piece of e and a piece of f. We repeat the procedure transfinitely.

Let then $\{y_i\}$ be a set in A with the properties $y_i = y_i^*$, y_i CC x^*x, $x^*xy_i^2$ is a non-zero projection e_i,

99

and $e_i e_j \neq 0$ for $i \neq j$, and suppose $\{y_i\}$ is maximal relative to these properties. Since $xe = x$, we have $e_i e = e_i$,
$e_i \leq e$. Let g be the LUB of $\{e_i\}$. Of course $g \leq e$. We
shall prove $g = e$.

A large part of the discussion takes place within the
commuting ring of $x^* x$, say B, and its center, say Z.
(Note that Z is the double commuting ring of $x^* x$ and that
both Z and B are Baer *-subrings of A.) We have that
$x^* x$, y_i, e_i and g all lie in Z.

We return to the proof that $g = e$. Suppose the contrary. Then $x^* x(1 - g) \neq 0$, for the vanishing of $x^* x(1 - g)$
implies $g \geq e$ since e is the right projection of $x^* x$. We
let $z = x(1 - g)$ and invoke the EP axiom to get a self-adjoint
element t with t CC $z^* z$ and $z^* z t^2 =$ a non-zero projection, say k. We claim that $(1 - g)t$ can be used to enlarge
the set $\{y_i\}$, a contradiction of maximality.

To see this, note first that $z^* z = (1 - g)x^* x(1 - g) \epsilon Z$.
Hence t commutes with everything in B and also lies in Z.
This shows that $(1 - g)t$ CC $x^* x$. It remains only to prove
$e_i k = 0$. Since $k = (1 - g)x^* x(1 - g)t^2$ and $e_i \leq g$ we get
$e_i k = 0$ at once.

We have thus proved $g = e$. Now write $w_i = xy_i$.

Then $w_i^* w_i = e_i$. Set $w_i w_i^* = f_i$. Since f is the left projection of x we have $fx = f$, hence $ff_i = f$, $f_i \le f$. Next we argue that f_i, f_j are orthogonal for $i \ne j$. Since $f_i f_j = w_i w_i^* w_j w_j^*$, it suffices to prove $w_i^* w_j = 0$, and since $w_i^* w_j = y_i x^* xy_j = x^* x e y_i y_j$ it suffices to prove $ey_i y_j = 0$. Now $x^* xy_i^2 = e_i$ is right-annihilated by $e - e_i$, whence $x^* x$ is right-annihilated by $y_i^2(e - e_i)$, whence $y_i^2(e - e_i) \in (1 - e)A$, since $1 - e$ is the right annihilating projection of x or $x^* x$.

Thus $ey_i^2(e - e_i) = 0$ so that $(e - e_i)y_i \cdot y_i(e - e_i) = 0$, and we have $ey_i = e_i y_i = y_i e_i = y_i e$. Now we can see that

$$ey_i y_j = y_i e_i e_j y_j = 0.$$

We have $e_i \sim f_i$ with $\{f_i\}$ a set of orthogonal projections all $\le f$. Let $h = \text{LUB}\{f_i\}$, and note $h \le f$. We have $g \sim h$, because additivity of equivalence is available from Theorems 54 and 62. Thus $e \lesssim f$.

In the proof of Theorem 65 below we shall in fact show that h is all of f. But this point need not detain us here. By symmetry, $f \lesssim e$, and by Theorem 41, $e \sim f$.

Remark. At this point we can exhibit a still different sequence of axioms and theorems, which gets all the main results, and is acceptable for the application to AW^*-

algebras.   Assume EP, SR and central additivity, get

general additivity as in Theorem 52, prove Theorem 63,

then get the parallelogram law as in exercises 1 and 2 of

§4.

15. ADDING PARTIAL ISOMETRIES

We raise the following question: when we establish additivity of equivalence can we add the actual partial isometries that occur? In detail: let $\{e_i\}$ be orthogonal with LUB e, $\{f_i\}$ orthogonal with LUB f, and let the partial isometry x_i link e_i, f_i in *-equivalence ($x_i x_i^* = e_i$, $x_i^* x_i = f_i$). Can we link e and f by a partial isometry x which in addition satisfies $e_i x = x f_i = x_i$? (We remark that when partial isometries are added in a W^*-algebra by taking a weak limit, such an element x is indeed constructed.)

The answer is "no". Let A be the ring of all bounded sequences of complex numbers with imaginary parts approaching 0; the involution is complex conjugation. (This example was mentioned in §1). Let $e_j = f_j =$ the sequence

with 1 in the j-th place, 0 elsewhere. For x_i we ob-
tusely take the j-th coordinate to be not 1 but $\sqrt{-1}$. These
x_j's cannote be added.

This example is abelian. It turns out that the abelian
case is essentially the only exception.

THEOREM 64.   Let A be a Baer *-ring satisfying the EP
and SR axioms and having no abelian direct summand $\neq 0$.
Let $\{e_i\}$ be orthogonal projections in A with LUB e,
$\{f_i\}$ orthogonal projections with LUB f. Assume that for
each i, e_i and f_i are *-equivalent via the partial isometry
x_i. Then there exists a partial isometry x satisfying
$$e_i x = x f_i = x_i .$$

Proof. By way of proof we ask the reader to check through
the proof of additivity of equivalence to see whether the
method actually yields an x as required. The crucial points
are:

(1) The x constructed in Theorem 30 is suitable.

(2) The move from e to a piece of $1 - f$ in
Theorem 50 and the II_1 case of Theorem 54 does not disturb
the property.

(3) There remains the pesky I_{inf} case.
When the argument in Theorem 54 is examined, it is seen

that the point to be settled comes down to the case where e

and f are abelian.   Now assume that there is no abelian

summand.   Then e is equivalent to a piece of 1 - f and all

is well.

The reader familiar with AW^*-algebras will easily

see that in that context abelian summands are not exceptional

and Theorem 64 holds unreservedly.

16. POLAR DECOMPOSITION

By polar decomposition we mean the result obtained
in Theorem 65.   In order to cover as much territory as
possible we do not exclude abelian summands but instead
assume that partial isometries can be added.

THEOREM 65.   Let B be a Baer *-ring satisfying the EP
and SR axioms.   Assume further that partial isometries can
be added in the sense of Theorem 64 (this assumption being
fulfilled in particular if A has no abelian direct summands).
Let x be any element in A and b any self-adjoint square
root of x^*x which CC x^*x.   Then x can be written x = wb
where w is a suitable partial isometry linking the left and
right projections of x.

Proof. We continue where the proof of Theorem 63 left off,

but first we make a fresh choice of the y_i's. Let B be the

commuting ring of x^*x; note that x^*x, y_i, e_i, b are all cen-

tral elements of B. We have that the component of x^*x in

$e_i B$ is invertible (with inverse y_i^2); therefore the same is

true of the component of b in $e_i B$. Let y_i' be the in-

verse of b in $e_i B$. Then y_i' may play the role of y_i, the

crucial point being that $(y_i')^2 x^*x = (y_i')^2 b^2$ is again e_i.

We change notation, replacing y_i' by y_i. Now let

w_i again be xy_i; w_i is a partial isometry linking e_i and f_i.

The LUB of $\{e_i\}$ is e, as proved in Theorem 63. By hy-

pothesis we have a "sum" w linking e and h; note in par-

ticular that $w_i = we_i = f_i w$. We shall prove that w fulfills

our requirements. We first check x = wb. Now wbe_i

$= we_i b = w_i b = xy_i b = xe_i$. Hence $(x - wb)e_i = 0$ for all i,

$(x - wb)e = 0$, x = wb since e is the right projection of both

x and b.

It remains to prove h = f. Since $f_i = w_i w_i^* = xy_i^2 x^*$

and y_i commutes with x^*x, we find that f_i commutes with

xx^* and hence so do h and f - h. Suppose $f - h \neq 0$. Then

also $(f - h)xx^* \neq 0$, since f is the left projection of xx^*.

By the EP axiom we find a self-adjoint element q such that q CC $(f - h)xx^*$ and $(f - h)xx^*q^2$ is a non-zero projection m. We have $m \leq f - h$ and evidently m commutes with xx^*.

Write $p = x^*q(f - h)$. We find $p^*p = m$, so pp^* is a non-zero projection, say n. Since pp^* ends in x we have $ne = n$, $n \leq e$. But we will get a contradiction by showing $ne_i = 0$ for all i (which would imply $ne = 0$, $n = 0$). For

$$ne_i = x^*(f - h)q^*x \cdot x^*xy_i^2$$

$$= x^* \cdot mxy_i^2 x^*x$$

$$= x^*mf_i x$$

since q commutes with xx^* and y_i commutes with x^*x. But $m \leq f - h$ implies $mf_i = 0$, and we have the desired contradiction.

The example used in the last section also serves as a counter-example to polar decomposition: take x to be the element with $\sqrt{-1}/j$ at the j-th coordinate.

17. STRONG SEMI-SIMPLICITY

For the theorems in the final two sections we resume the axiomatic point of view.

For Theorem 66 we appear to need two additional axioms:

(J) Any non-zero two-sided ideal contains a non-zero projection.

(K) If I is a two-sided ideal, $e \in I$ and $e \sim f$, then $f \in I$.

We note that (J) is implied by regularity or by the EP axiom, and that (K) is satisfied by actual equivalence, and all the more so by *-equivalence. (See exercise 5 in §2.)

THEOREM 66.   Let A be a Baer *-ring satisfying axiom J.

Assume that A has an equivalence relation $\sim$ satisfying

axioms A-F and K, and that A is finite relative to $\sim$.

Then (1) any non-zero two-sided ideal in A contains a non-

zero central projection, (2) A is strongly semi-simple (the

intersection of the two-sided maximal ideals in A is 0).

Proof. (1).   Let I be a non-zero two-sided ideal in A.   By

axiom J, I contains a non-zero projection e_1.   Let

$e_1, \ldots, e_n$ be a maximal set of orthogonal projections equiv-

alent to e_1 (necessarily finite since A is finite).   Let

$f = 1 - (e_1 + \ldots + e_n)$.   Apply comparability (Theorem 35) to

e_1 and f, getting a central projection u with $uf \lesssim ue_1$,

$(1 - u)f \gtrsim (1 - u)e_1$.   We cannot have u = 0, for then a

suitable piece of f could be used to enlarge $\{e_i\}$.   We have

$ue_1 \in I$ and by axiom K, $ue_2, \ldots, ue_n$, uf all lie in I.

Hence $u \in I$.

(2).   The deduction of (2) from (1) is pure ring

theory (and easy).

EXERCISE. Let A satisfy the hypotheses of Theorem 66

and in addition be a factor of type II_1. Prove that A is a

simple ring.

18. THE LATTICE OF PROJECTIONS

The material in this final section is adapted from [5, §6].

THEOREM 67. Let A be a Baer *-ring with an equivalence relation satisfying axioms A-F and H. Then the finite projections in A form a modular lattice.

<u>Proof</u>. By Theorem 56 the union of two finite projections is finite. This suffices to demonstrate that the finite projections form a sublattice of the lattice of all projections.

Let e, f, g be projections with $e \leq g$. We form the two expressions relevant for the modular law: $h = (e \cup f) \cap g$ and $k = e \cup (f \cap g)$. Both h and k have the property that their union with f is $e \cup f$, and their intersection with f is

$f \cap g$.   By two applications of axiom H:

$$h - (f \cap g) \sim (e \cup f) - f \sim k - (f \cap g),$$

whence $h \sim k$.   In any lattice we have $h \geq k$.   Finiteness of h yields $h = k$, proving the theorem.

THEOREM 68.   Let A be a finite Baer *-ring with an equivalence relation satisfying axioms A-F and either axiom G or axiom H.   Let $\{e_\alpha\}$ be a well-ordered ascending set of projections in A, with LUB e.   Suppose f is a projection satisfying $e_\alpha \leq f$ for all α.   Then $e \stackrel{\sim}{\leq} f$.

Proof.   We may assume without loss of generality that when λ is a limit ordinal, e_λ is the LUB of the preceding e_α's. We proceed to construct a well-ordered ascending set of projections $\{f_\alpha\}$ with the properties: (1) $e_\alpha \sim f_\alpha$ for all α, (2) $f_\alpha \leq f$ for all α, (3) when λ is a limit ordinal, f_λ is the LUB of the preceding f_α's.   Suppose f_α has been constructed for $\alpha < \beta$.

Case I. β is a limit ordinal.   We take f_β = LUB of the preceding f_α's.   Then properties (2) and (3) are clear.

To verify (1) we note that f_β is the LUB of the orthogonal projections f_1 and $\{f_{\alpha+1} - f_\alpha, \ \alpha < \beta\}$; likewise e_β is the LUB of e_1 and $\{e_{\alpha+1} - e_\alpha, \ \alpha < \beta\}$. Uniqueness of subtraction (see exercise 2 in §12) tells us $e_{\alpha+1} - e_\alpha \sim f_{\alpha+1} - f_{\alpha+1} - f_\alpha$. By additivity (Theorem 52 or 54 as appropriate), $e_\beta \sim f_\beta$.

     Case II. β not a limit ordinal. By hypothesis there is an equivalence between e_β and a portion of f; suppose this induces an equivalence of $e_{\beta-1}$ and g, $e_\beta - e_{\beta-1}$ and $f - g$. By uniqueness of subtraction, $f - f_{\beta-1} \sim f - g$. Hence $e_\beta - e_{\beta-1} \stackrel{<}{\sim} f - f_{\beta-1}$, i.e. $e_\beta - e_{\beta-1} \sim h$ with $h \leq f - f_{\beta-1}$. We take f_β to be $f_{\beta-1} + h$. Maintenance of the three properties is clear.

     When the construction is completed, we have, by Theorem 52 or 54, $e \sim$ LUB of $\{f_\alpha\}$, and hence $e \stackrel{<}{\sim} f$.

THEOREM 69. Let A be a finite Baer *-ring with an equivalence relation satisfying axioms A-F and H. Then the lattice of projections in A is a continuous geometry.

Proof. The only thing needing proof is the continuity axiom for continuous geometries. By duality, we need only consider the one that concerns LUB's. Let then $\{e_\alpha\}$ be a well-ordered ascending set of projections with LUB e; let f be another projection, and let the LUB of $\{e_\alpha \cap f\}$ be g. Our task is to prove $h = (e \cap f) - g = 0$. Write $k_\alpha = (e \cap f) \cup e_\alpha$. By axiom H, we have the equivalence in the middle of

$$h \leq (e \cap f) - (e_\alpha \cap f) \sim k_\alpha - e_\alpha \leq e - e_\alpha .$$

We claim that $e_\alpha \lesssim e - h$ for all α. Otherwise by Theorem 57 there would be a direct summand where $e - h$ is equivalent to a proper part of e_α. Adding this to $h \leq e - e_\alpha$ gives us a contradiction to the finiteness of e. Hence $e_\alpha \lesssim e - h$ for all α. By Theorem 68, $e \lesssim e - h$, and by finiteness, $h = 0$.

In a continuous geometry, the center is defined as the set of elements with unique complements, and equivalence is defined as the possession of a common complement. In the next two theorems we substantially identify these concepts with the corresponding ones in suitable Baer *-rings.

THEOREM 70. Let A be a Baer *-ring which satisfies axiom E relative to *-equivalence or axioms E and F relative to ordinary equivalence. Then a projection in A is central if and only if it has a unique complement.

Proof. That a central projection has unique complement is immediate and requires no hypotheses at all.

Conversely suppose the projection e has a unique complement, necessarily 1 - e. We shall prove that e is central. Orthogonal comparability (Theorem 35) is applicable to e and 1 - e. The setup is symmetric between e and 1 - e (the mapping sending any projection h into 1 - h is an anti-automorphism of the lattice of projections); thus after dropping to a direct summand we may assume e ~ f (resp. e $\overset{*}{\sim}$ f) with f ≤ 1 - e. Let g be the projection constructed in Theorem 29 or in exercise 4 of §4, and let k = g + (1 - e - f). We leave it to the reader to verify that k is a complement of e; that is, e ∩ k = 0, e ∪ k = 1. Hence k = 1 - e, from which it follows readily that e = 0.

Suppose, without being precise, we are in a setup where the parallelogram law holds, and suppose e and f have g as a common complement.   Then e and g are both equivalent to 1 - f and hence to each other.   The converse is true only for finite projections.

THEOREM 71.   Let A be a Baer *-ring with an equivalence relation satisfying axioms A-F and H.   Then any two finite equivalent projections have a common complement.

Proof. Let e and f be equivalent finite projections.   Since we can work within e ∪ f we can assume the whole ring is finite (Theorem 56).   Then (Theorem 69) the lattice of projections is a continuous geometry.   We apply the comparability theorem of continuous geometry: after dropping to a direct summand we may assume e and g have a common complement, where g ≤ f.   As remarked above, e ~ g.   By finiteness g = f.

Remarks. Fillmore [3] has shown that in W^*-algebras two projections have a common complement if and only if they are unitarily equivalent.   Does this generalize ?

APPENDIX I. THE AXIOMS OF LOOMIS AND

MAEDA

Independently, and about at the same time, Loomis [9] and Maeda [10] studied a setup in which an equivalence relation was postulated. Their framework was lattice-theoretic rather than ring-theoretic: for Loomis ortho-modular lattices, for Maeda a somewhat wider class of lattices. But the main difference between their work and the present work, or Maeda's second paper [11], was their out-right assumption of unrestricted additivity of equivalence. It is interesting to note Halperin's suggestion [Math. Reviews 17(1956), 514-5] that it would be desirable to assume only orthogonal additivity and deduce general additivity as a theorem. Of course the main purpose of Loomis and Maeda was to show how their axioms sufficed to develop dimension

theory. We have chosen to stop the theory (in §18) at the
point where we reached a continuous geometry; but the
reader should not suppose that the thing to do next is to wade
through the long, intricate theory of continuous geometries.
If he wishes to go on to dimension theory, the accounts by
Loomis and Maeda are quite suitable. For a discerning
account of these matters see also Holland's survey [4] of
orthomodular lattices.

Maeda's subsequent paper [11] is very close in
spirit to the account given here. If we ignore minor nuances,
the chief difference is our use of central additivity (axiom G)
as an alternate road to all the target theorems. As Maeda
acknowledges, his paper is based on the papers [5],[8] and
on the first edition of Rings of Operators.

Maharam's complete structure theory of abstract
measure algebras [12] is also based on a postulated equivalence relation. As noted in §4, axiom B is the one that
makes this work diverge decisively from hers.

APPENDIX II. W^*-ALGEBRAS AND AW^*-ALGEBRAS

A W^*-algebra (ring of operators, von Newmann algebra) is a weakly closed self-adjoint algebra of operators on a Hilbert space.   An AW^*-algebra is a C^*-algebra (uniformly closed self-adjoint algebra of operators on a Hilbert space) which is also a Baer ring.   In the commutative case the difference is this: for an AW^*-algebra the projections form an arbitrary complete Boolean algebra which need not be a measure algebra.   It is a standing conjecture that an AW^*-algebra is W^* if its center is W^*.

For a person who knows C^*-algebra theory, the following is a relatively short way to enter the W^* and AW^* circle of ideas.   Let A be a W^*-algebra.   Let T be a positive self-adjoint operator in A.   Let E be the projection on the closure of the range of T. We wish to prove

$E \in A$. Embed T in a commutative C^*-algebra B, thought

of as continuous functions on a compact Hausdorff space X.

Let f_n be a continuous real function on X satisfying:

$0 \leq f_n \leq 1$, $f_n = 1$ where $T \geq 1/n$, $f_n = 0$ where $T = 0$. We

also arrange that the f's increase: $f_1 \leq f_2 \leq f_3 \dots$. It is

elementary to verify that $f_n(T)$ converges strongly (and all

the more so weakly) to E. This is the key point in proving

that a W^*-algebra is AW^*, the rest being quite routine.

(Of course one could instead simply quote the spectral

theorem.)

One might think of AW^*-algebras (and more generally

Baer rings) as corresponding to the intrinsic structure

theory of W^*-algebras. From this one goes on to represen-

tation or spatial theory, concerned with how a W^*-algebra

acts on a given Hilbert space. As an illustration we shall

sketch the spatial theory of W^*-algebras of type I. For full

accounts the reader should turn to the various expositions

of W^*-algebras available in the literature.

The first theorem to be proved is the following: let

A be a commutative W^*-algebra of operators on a Hilbert

space H. Suppose A admits a cyclic vector x. Then:
A is maximal commutative.

Our hypothesis means that Ax is dense in H. If
Ax actually equals H, the result is a purely algebraic
triviality. The point however is that we do have Ax = H
"locally", i.e., for any $y \in H$ we have -- after dropping
to a non-zero direct summand and changing notation --
Cx = y for a suitable $C \in A$. This is seen by borrowing
some devices from measure theory. Assume $\|x\| = 1$. We
have $B_n \in A$ with $B_n x \to y$ and $r_n = \|B_{n+1} x - B_n x\|$ as
small as we please. Let $C_n = (B_{n+1} - B_n)^*(B_{n+1} - B_n)/r_n^2$,
and note $(C_n x, x) = 1$. Let $E_n \in A$ be the maximal projection satisfying $E_n A_n \geq 2^{n+1} E_n$. Then $(E_n x, x) \leq 1/2^{n+1}$
and ΣE_n cannot equal 1. We drop to the direct summand
given by $1 - \Sigma E_n$ and change notation. This results in
$\|C_n\| \leq 2^{n+1}$. By suitable choice of r_n we have
$\|B_{n+1} - B_n\|$ arbitrarily small and $\|B_n\|$ bounded. We
now see that for any $z \in H$, $B_n z$ converges. For take
$D \in A$ with $\|Dx - z\|$ small and estimate $B_m z - B_n z$ by

$$B_m z - B_n z = D(B_m - B_n)x + (B_m - B_n)(z - Dx).$$

Define C, a strong limit of $\{B_n\}$, by $Cz = \lim B_n z$. Then $C \in A$ and $Cx = y$.

One can now swiftly prove that if A is a W^*-algebra of type I the commuting algebra A' is again of type I. For the problem reduces to the case where A is commutative, then to the case where there is a cyclic vector under A, in which case A' = A.

Next theorem: let A and B be maximal commutative W^*-algebras on Hilbert spaces H and K. Let ϕ be an isomorphism of A onto B. Then ϕ can be implemented by a unitary map of H onto K.

By dropping to direct summands we get A and B to admit cyclic vectors x and y. The plan now is to send Tx into $\phi(T)y$. This map need not be continuous, but simple estimates show that more dropping to direct summands makes it continuous both ways. A polar decomposition then does the trick.

The full spatial description of W^*-algebras of type I is now at hand. One decomposes the algebra A and its commuting algebra A' into homogeneous parts, in the manner of Theorem 46. On each such "doubly homogeneous" part the invariants are a pair of cardinal numbers and the

common center of A   and A'.

APPENDIX III. REAL AW*-ALGEBRAS

All studies of W* and AW*-algebras have hitherto assumed complex scalars. In this appendix we take the first steps in a theory that assumes only real scalars. This would, for instance, be pertinent for a multiplicity theory of operators on a real Hilbert space.

It is clear what a real W*-algebra is: a weakly closed self-adjoint algebra of operators on a real Hilbert space.

Before saying what a real AW*-algebra should be, we define a real C*-algebra: either concretely as a norm-closed self-adjoint algebra of operators on a real Hilbert space, or abstractly as a Banach algebra over the real numbers and an involution satisfying $\|xx^*\| = \|x\|^2$ with the invertibility of $1 + xx^*$ (in the real case we cannot omit

129

this last postulate).   Then: a real AW*-algebra is a real

C*-algebra which is also a Baer ring.   Consequences: it is

a Baer *-ring satisfying all the axioms from A to K, plus

the EP and SR axioms.   But a real AW*-algebra need not

satisfy additivity of partial isometries or polar decompo-

sition (see the example mentioned in §15 and §16).   Perhaps

addition of partial isometries should be incorporated into the

definition of a real AW*-algebra.

Needless to say, a real W*-algebra is real AW*, and

moreover it does satisfy additivity of partial isometries.

The first step in the study of real AW*-algebras con-

cerns the decomposition of the center under the involution,

and can be taken for suitable Baer rings.

THEOREM A.   Let A be a Baer *-ring satisfying the EP

and SR axioms. If A has an abelian direct summand,

assume further that partial isometries in A can be added.

Then A can be written $B \oplus C$, where * leaves the center

of B elementwise fixed, and the center of C contains an

element i satisfying $i^2 = -1$, $i^* = -i$.

Proof. If every element of the center Z of A is self-

adjoint, B is all of A. Otherwise we pick $t \in Z$ with

$x = t - t^* \neq 0$. Pick y by the SR axiom: xx^*y^2 = a non-zero

projection u, y CC xx^*. Evidently y and u lie in Z. In

the summand uA, the element xy furnishes the desired

element, for $(xy)^2$ = -u and $(xy)^*$ = -xy. Furthermore

xy is a partial isometry. The ability to add partial iso-

metries is just what is needed to continue the procedure

transfinitely.

If the decomposition in Theorem A is applied to a

real AW*-algebra, the component C is a complex AW*-

algebra. Thus the discussion need only continue for B,

which we might call "purely real".

We turn to algebras of type I, and wish to prove that

they can be decomposed further into two parts, the first

being purely real in a still stronger sense, and the second

"pure quaternion". Before doing this, we prove a theorem

on C*-algebras.

THEOREM B. Let A be a real C*-algebra with no non-

zero nilpotent elements. Then every self-adjoint element

of A is central.

Remark. For complex C^*-algebras this has been a "folk theorem" since the early 1950's.

Proof. It suffices to show that for any primitive ideal P in A, the self-adjoint elements of A/P are scalars. If we suppose the contrary, then we can find a self-adjoint y in A/P with 0 and 1 in the spectrum of y. Let x in A map on y; let f and g be continuous real functions defined on the real line such that $f(1) = 1$, f vanishes outside a small neighborhood of 1, $g(0) = 1$, g vanishes outside a small neighborhood of 0. Let $a = f(x)$, $b = g(x)$. Then $ab = 0$, and it follows from the hypothesis of no nilpotent elements that $bAa = 0$. We pass to the promitive ring A/P and deduce that $f(y)$ or $g(y)$ must be 0, a contradiction since each has 1 in its spectrum.

With this C^*-algebra information at hand, we return to Baer rings. In connection with Theorem C, we note that the hypothesis that 2 is invertible is fulfilled in suitable Baer *-rings with no abelian direct summands (see exercise 13 in §1).

THEOREM C.   Let A be an abelian Baer *-ring satisfying

the EP and SR axioms.   Assume that partial isometries can

be added in A, and that 2 is invertible in A.   Assume that

the center Z of A is exactly the set of self-adjoint elements

in A.   Then $A = D \oplus E$, where * is the identity on D and E

is the ring of (ordinary) quaternions over its center.

Proof. If * is the identity on A, all is done.   Otherwise we

get a non-zero skew element x and adjust it as in the proof

of Theorem A.   In detail we have $y^* = y$ (so that y is cen-

tral), $-y^2 x^2 = $ a non-zero projection u.   In the summand

uA we have $(yx)^2 = -u$.   We are able to continue the pro-

cess transfinitely.   The upshot is that we may assume (after

a change of notation) that A contains an element i satis-

fying $i^2 = -1$, $i^* = -i$.

Let t be any skew element in A.   Then $a = ti + it$

is self-adjoint, hence central.   If we write

$t = -ai/2 + (t + ai/2)$ we recognize that we have written t

as the sum of a central multiple of i and a skew element

that anti-commutes with i.   In a suitable direct summand,

the element $t + ai/2$ can be normalized, the way i was, to

a skew element j with $j^2 = -1$, $ij = -ji$. Continued transfinitely, this process must go all the way, for otherwise in
some direct summand the component of i would be a non-
self-adjoint central element. We set $k = ij$, and note
$k^2 = -1$, $k^* = -k$, $jk = -kj = i$, etc.

We wish to show that $1, i, j, k$ span A over Z. In
view of the equation $2x = (x + x^*) + (x - x^*)$, we can assume
x skew. In view of the decomposition in the preceding paragraph, we can further assume that x anti-commutes with i.
The element xj commutes with i. Hence by the decomposition again, $xj \in Z + Zi$ and $x \in Zj + Zk$.

We leave to the reader the routine verification that
A is a free Z-module on the basis $1, i, j, k$.

APPENDIX IV. ALGEBRAIC SIMPLICITY OF

THE FULL LINEAR GROUP

Let A be a W^* factor of type II_1. Let G be its full linear group, i. e. the multiplicative group of all invertible elements in A. Kadison [Trans. Amer. Math. Soc. 76(1954), 66-91] proved that, after some trimming at top and bottom, G is <u>topologically</u> simple in the sense that it has no normal subgroup closed in the norm topology.

In the middle 1950's I noted that certain modified arguments could strengthen this to <u>algebraic</u> simplicity. On reviewing these arguments recently, I observed that the matter could even be made a piece of pure algebra, at the expense of still one more axiom, which I call the <u>spectral axiom</u>.

In this final appendix we state the theorem and sketch the proof.

Kadison also proved the topological simplicity of the unitary group modulo its center [Trans. Amer. Math. Soc. 72(1952), 386-399]. Because of the lack of anything resembling transvections in the unitary group, the present method yields nothing, and the algebraic simplicity of the (suitably trimmed) unitary group is an open question.

The idea behind the spectral axiom is to extract the essential point in the statement that a W^*-algebra is generated by its projections. Our substitute for W^* is to take a commuting ring S' (inside a fixed larger Baer *-ring), and we ask the projections to generate in the sense they determine what commutes with S'.

SPECTRAL AXIOM. Let A be a Baer *-ring. For a self-adjoint subset S of A we write S' for the commuting ring of S, S'' for the commuting ring of S'. We say that A satisfies the spectral axiom if for any S the commuting ring of the set of projections in S' is again S''.

Any complex AW^*-algebra satisfies the spectral
axiom. A real AW^*-algebra (or even W^*-algebra) need not.
Probably a modest change in the axiom is all that is needed
to get Theorem D to work, but I have not looked into it.

THEOREM D. Let A be a Baer *-ring which is a factor of
type II_1 and satisfies the EP, SR, and the spectral axioms.
Let G be the full linear group of A, H = [GG] the commutator subgroup of G. Then: any normal subgroup of H
is either contained in the center Z of A or equals H. In
particular, $H/(Z \cap H)$ is simple.

Outline of Proof. It is easiest to phrase the proof in terms
of dimension theory, but a few simple remarks can replace
a full fledged development of dimension theory. We shall
write D(e) for the dimension of a projection e. For a ϵ G,
we find it convenient to introduce a symbol for the dimension
of the right or left projection of a - 1 (note that by Theorem
63 these two projections are equivalent and therefore have
the same dimension); our notation will be $\Delta(a)$. We observe
that $\Delta(ab) \leq \Delta(a) + \Delta(b)$.

Let N be a normal subgroup of H, $N \not\subset Z$. We have to prove $N = H$.

By a transvection (relative to a set of matrix units) we mean as usual a matrix having the form identity plus a single element in some (i, j) entry $(i \neq j)$. Our method of proof will be to show first that N contains a single trans-vection, then an abundance of transvections, and finally all commutators.

We start with any $x \in N - Z$. It is easily seen that there exists an element $y \in H$ such that $t = xyx^{-1}y^{-1} \not\subset Z$ and moreover that such a y can be picked with $\Delta(y)$ arbi-trarily small. Since $\Delta(t) \leq \Delta(xyx^{-1}) + \Delta(y^{-1}) = 2\Delta(y)$, the resulting $\Delta(t)$ can also be arranged to be arbitrarily small. Suppose $\Delta(t) \leq 1/n$. Then we can construct (see exercise 12 in §3) a set of n by n *-matrix units so that t has the form

$$ t = \begin{pmatrix} a & & & O \\ & 1 & & \\ & & \ddots & \\ O & & & 1 \end{pmatrix} $$

where of course $a \neq 1$. We suppose $n \geq 3$; then, as is well

known, all transvections are commutators. Now in view of

the equation

$$\begin{pmatrix} a & 0 \\ 0 & 1 \end{pmatrix}\begin{pmatrix} 1 & b \\ 0 & 1 \end{pmatrix}\begin{pmatrix} a^{-1} & 0 \\ 0 & 1 \end{pmatrix}\begin{pmatrix} 1 & -b \\ 0 & 1 \end{pmatrix} = \begin{pmatrix} 1 & ab - b \\ 0 & 1 \end{pmatrix} ,$$

by commutating t with a suitable transvection we prove

that N contains a transvection. Since A is a simple ring,

it follows that N contains all transvections, relative to

this fixed set of *-matrix units (here we are again using

$n \geq 3$). A standard computation then shows that N contains

the matrix

$$\begin{pmatrix} c^{-1}d^{-1}cd & & & O \\ & 1 & & \\ & & \ddots & \\ O & & & 1 \end{pmatrix}$$

for any c, d.

Now we wish to make the switch to other sets of

*-matrix units. This would be immediate if N were nor-

mal in G. Since N is only known to be normal in H, we

yield a little ground. Lemma: if e and f are projections with $D(e) = D(f) \leq 1/6$, then e and f are conjugate in H.

For if $g = e \cup f$ then $D(g) \leq 1/3$. Inside the ring gAg we

have e and f conjugate in the full linear group. We blow

up the conjugating element to a 3 by 3 matrix of the form

$$\begin{pmatrix} x & 0 & 0 \\ 0 & x^{-1} & 0 \\ 0 & 0 & 1 \end{pmatrix}$$

noting that this matrix lies in H (it is a product of trans-

vections, and the latter are commutators).

So: if we take $n = 6$ we can conclude that N contains

all transvections relative to <u>every</u> set of 6 by 6 *-matrix

units. And we have as an immediate corollary: if $\Delta(a)$ and

$\Delta(b)$ are $\leq 1/12$ then $aba^{-1}b^{-1} \in N$.

We are approaching the end of the proof. Given any

r and s in G we have to prove $rsr^{-1}s^{-1} \in N$. The method

will be to use polar decomposition, and to invoke the spectral

axiom to effect a sort of diagonalization of the self-adjoint

and unitary components.

Let $x \in A$ be either self-adjoint or unitary. Let e

be a projection commuting with x, $e \neq 0$. We wish to prove that there exists a projection commuting with x and lying strictly between 0 and e. Suppose the contrary. We let S denote the set consisting of x, x^* and e. Both the commuting ring S' and the double commuting ring S" contain e as a central projection. Our hypothesis says that the only projections in eS' are 0 and e. From this it follows from the spectral axiom that eS" is all of S". But then x commutes with all projections $\leq$ e after all.

By the usual kind of transfinite repetition we can proceed to show that x commutes with projections of all possible dimensions, and further that for any n there exist n equivalent orthogonal projections adding up to 1 and commuting with x. We choose to do this with n = 12.

Now let r be arbitrary in G. Polar decomposition (Theorem 65) expresses r as $r = r_1 r_2$ with r_1 self-adjoint and r_2 unitary. We decompose r_1 and r_2 as just described. The upshot is that r can be written as the product of 24 elements, each having $\Delta \leq 1/12$. We do the same for a second element $s \in G$. As we have seen, the commutator of each constituent of r with each one of s lies in N. Furthermore the condition $\Delta(a) \leq 1/12$ is invariant under conjugation by elements of G; this follows

from the fact that the SR axiom makes equivalence imply

*-equivalence (Theorem 27).　We conclude $rsr^{-1}s^{-1} \in N$,

as needed.

BIBLIOGRAPHY

(This bibliography is limited to items to which there is an actual reference. The reader is strongly urged to familiarize himself with the basic papers of Murray and von Neumann, and to go on from there to the later literature on W^*-algebras.)

1. I. Amemiya and I. Halperin, Complemented modular lattices, Can. J. of Math. 11(1959), 481-520.

2. P. Fillmore, The dimension theory of certain cardinal algebras, Trans. Amer. Math. Soc. 117(1965), 21-36.

3. _____, Perspectivity in projection lattices, Proc. Amer. Math. Soc. 16(1965), 383-7.

4. S. Holland, The current interest in ortho-modular lattices, to appear in Trends in Lattice Theory, Van Nostrand.

5. I. Kaplansky, Projections in Banach algebras, Ann. of Math. 53(1951), 235-249.

6. _____, Algebras of type I, Ann. of Math. 56(1952), 460-472.

7. I. Kaplansky, Modules over operator algebras, Amer. J. of Math. 75(1953), 839-858.

8. _____, Any orthocomplemented complete modular lattice is a continuous geometry, Ann. of Math. 61(1955), 524-541.

9. L. Loomis, The lattice theoretic background of the dimension theory of operator algebras, Mem. Amer. Math. Soc. No. 18 (1955), 36 pp.

10. S. Maeda, Dimension functions on certain general lattices, J. Sci. Hiroshima Univ. Ser. A-I Math. 19(1955), 211-237.

11. _____, On the lattice of projections of a Baer *-ring, J. Sci. Hiroshima Univ. Ser. A-I Math. 22(1958), 76-88.

12. D. Maharam, The representation of abstract measure functions, Trans. Amer. Math. Soc. 65(1949), 279-330.

13. D. Ornstein, Dual vector spaces, Ann. of Math. 69(1959), 520-534.

14. C. E. Rickart, Banach algebras with an adjoint operation, Ann. of Math. 47(1946), 528-550.

15.   L. A. Shornjakov, Complemented modular lattices and

regular rings, Moscow, 1961.   English translation,

Edinburgh-London, 1964.

INDEX OF AXIOMS

INDEX

Abelian, 10, 104, 107

Annihilator, i, 1

AW^*-algebra , ii, 75, 81, 89, 97, 102, 105, 123-7, 137

    real —— , 6, 129-134, 137

Baer ring, ii, 3

    center of ——, 8

Baer *-ring, ii, 13, 27

Baer *-subring, 29

Boolean algebra, 8, 123

C^*-algebra, i, 123, 132

    real ——, 129, 131

Central additivity, 75-80, 89, 97, 102, 122

Central cover, 9, 23

CC (commutes with everything that commutes with), 35, 89

Comparability, 53-4, 87, 98

Continuous geometry, 117, 122

Dimension, 121, 137

Dual vector spaces, 5

Equivalence

    —— of idempotents, iv, 22